Guns

THE DEVELOPMENT OF FIREARMS,
AIR GUNS AND CARTRIDGES

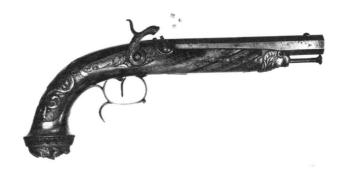

Guns

THE DEVELOPMENT OF FIREARMS, AIR GUNS AND CARTRIDGES

Told in Pictures

By WARREN MOORE

GROSSET & DUNLAP   *Publishers*
New York

C 608 2010 1

PRINTED IN THE UNITED STATES OF AMERICA

CONTENTS

ACKNOWLEDGMENTS

The most enjoyable part of compiling the information for this book came from the wonderful cooperation which I received from other gun collectors and from historians, many of whom were strangers to me. Everyone whom I contacted, both here and abroad, gave generously of his time in supplying me with photographs and other information which I requested.

The person to whom I am most deeply indebted is Lewis Winant. Mr. Winant was most helpful during many visits, as well as in much correspondence with him. His latest book, Early Percussion Firearms, was of invaluable assistance to me, and was used more than any other book. In my opinion, this is one of the finest books ever written on firearms, and it is recommended reading to those who wish to learn more about one of the most interesting phases in the development of firearms.

Dr. W. R. Funderburg very generously sent me photographs of a number of pieces from his collection, and took the time to write many letters giving me much historical data associated with the pictures. Two pistols from Dr. Funderburg's collection, the Joseph Manton tube lock, and the Baker combination flint and percussion, are pictured in the book.

Others who furnished me with pictures and information are listed as follows:

W. Reid, H. M. Tower of London, Crown Copyright Reserved — Puckle gun and air gun with reservoir-surrouding-barrel.

J. Laing, Royal United Service Institution, London, England — Snaphaunce revolver.

Professor E. Trincanato, Director, Palazzo Ducale, Venice, Italy — Three barrel matchlock revolver.

J. Paulsen, Director, Tojhusmuseet, Copenhagen, Denmark — Hand cannon and snaphaunce revolving petronel.

Thomas E. Hall, Firearms Historian, Olin-Mathieson Chemical Corp. — Forsyth fulminate pistol.

R. Lawrence Wilson, Wadsworth Atheneum, Hartford, Conn. — Collier flintlock revolver.

Smithsonian Institution — Crispin revolver.

Colt Collection — .45 caliber National Teat revolver and Polain revolver.

Glode Requa — Cased set of Colt Paterson percussion revolvers.

Paul Westergard — Outside lock air gun.

John L. Barry, Jr. — Smith & Wesson revolver, Model 1, Issue 1.

Henry M. Stewart — Thuer Colt revolver.

The balance of the guns shown in this book are from the author's collection, and the photography for these was done by Henry Bedlivy.

Last, but not least, I would like to thank my wife, Jean, for the many hours she spent in helping me to put this book together.

FOREWORD

My purpose in writing this book has been to present, in digest form, the development story of firearms, air guns and cartridges. Brief accounts of the Smith and Wesson partnership and revolver history have also been included.

After acquiring my first flintlock pistol fifteen years ago, I recall the difficulty experienced in grasping the overall development sequence of the various ignition systems, such as the wheel lock, tube lock, pill lock, etc. It is hoped that this condensed presentation will help clarify the development story, not only for gun collectors, but also for sportsmen and others with even a passing interest in guns.

I have derived a great deal of pleasure from collecting old guns, and in particular was fascinated with the story associated with the evolution of firearms. Others, I feel, will also find this subject an interesting one, and possibly the reading of this book will kindle a spark in others to pursue the matter further by reading some of the more than 3,000 excellent books relating to the arms field.

WARREN MOORE

Ramsey, New Jersey

PART I

The Evolution of Firearms

This section of the book presents the various types of ignition systems that were used on firearms from the primitive hand cannon of around 1350 to the first automatic pistol of 1893. Pistols are used in this text to illustrate the steps in development; however, shoulder arms, such as long guns and rifles, were also made that were equipped with the same types of firing mechanisms.

It is interesting to observe how each weapon in this series of arms progression is an improvement over its predecessor, but still did not measure up to the perfection that was desired. Even today designers and technicians are engaged in the endless task of trying to produce the ultimate in firearms.

CENTURY				
14th	1 HAND CANNON			F I R E
	2 MATCHLOCK			
	3 WHEELLOCK			P Y R I T E A N D F L I N T
	4 SNAPHAUNCE			
	5 DOG LOCK			
	6 MIQUELET LOCK			
	7 FLINTLOCK			
	8 DUAL IGNITION			F U L M I N A T E
	9 FULMINATE POWDER			
	10 PILL or PELLET LOCK			
	11 TUBE LOCK			

FIREARMS DEVELOPMENT

the first Automatic Pistol of 1893

	12 PATCH LOCK			F U L M I N A T E
	13 PERCUSSION CAP			
	14 TAPE PRIMER			
	15 DISC PRIMER			
19th C E N T U R Y	16 FIRST CARTRIDGE (SELF-CONTAINED)			S E L F - C O N T A I N E D C A R T R I D G E
	17 NEEDLE FIRE			
	18 PIN FIRE			
	19 VOLCANIC			
	20 B-B CAP			
	21 METALLIC CARTRIDGE			
	22 AUTOMATIC			

1 HAND CANNON

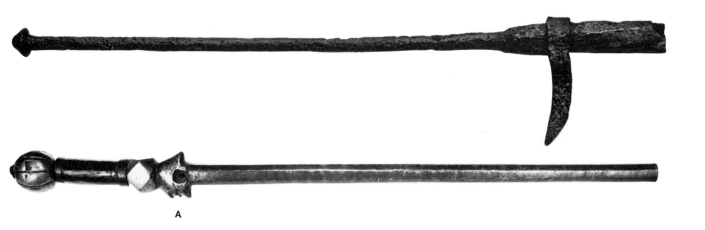

A

THE ORIGIN of gunpowder is lost in antiquity. Some time before the year 1249, Roger Bacon of Merton College, Oxford, England, first wrote the formula for gunpowder. However, he did not claim to be the inventor. After years of experimentation, he arrived at a mixture of saltpeter, charcoal and sulfur, in a ratio which was written in a secret code.

By 1300, true cannons appeared, but it was about fifty years later before the first hand firearm was put into use. These hand firearms were simply smaller versions of the big cannons, and consequently were called hand cannons. Firing was achieved by inserting a live coal, red hot wire, or match through the touchhole located at the closed end of the tube.

There are very few known specimens in the world today of fourteenth century hand cannons. The Historical Museum of Stockholm, Sweden has a specimen dated about 1350, and the Tojhusmuseet of Copenhagen, Denmark has one dated approximately 1400. Firearms of this type were made in the Orient as late as the eighteenth century.

The top picture is the Vedelspang gun from the Tojhusmuseet collection, and dates from about 1400. The short 8-inch barrel terminates in a long iron rod which acts as a breech plug and stock. The hook around the barrel serves to limit the recoil. This gun was found at the site of a castle which was built in 1416 and destroyed in 1426. All of the early hand cannons had touchholes on the top, and it was only late in the sixteenth century that the touchhole was moved to the right side and a powder pan was attached to the barrel.

The bottom hand cannon in the picture above is Chinese, made during the latter part of the eighteenth century. Although it was made almost 450 years after the first European hand cannon, its construction and method of firing are identical.

2 MATCHLOCK

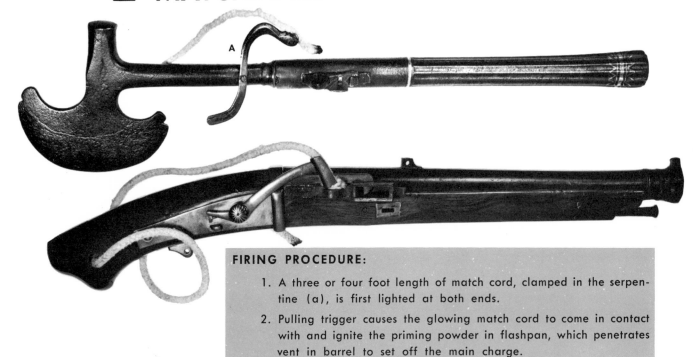

A

FIRING PROCEDURE:

1. A three or four foot length of match cord, clamped in the serpentine (a), is first lighted at both ends.

2. Pulling trigger causes the glowing match cord to come in contact with and ignite the priming powder in flashpan, which penetrates vent in barrel to set off the main charge.

THE TRANSITION from hand cannon to matchlock began about 1400 with the use of an S-shaped piece of metal called a serpentine. This device was pivoted at the center and attached to the side of the gun. At the same time, the touchhole was moved from the top of the barrel to the right side and provided with a pan to hold priming powder. A two or three yard length of matchcord, consisting of strands of twisted cotton, hemp, or flax, and soaked in a solution of saltpeter for slow and steady burning, was clamped into the serpentine. By raising the lower end of the serpentine, the lighted matchcord was guided into the powder pan. This serpentine was later connected to a trigger through a link arrangement, thus making the matchlock system the first true gunlock.

Although the matchlock was an advancement over its predecessor, the primitive hand cannon, it had many disadvantages. These were: its dependence upon a lighted match, coupled with the fact that rain and high winds rendered it useless; the necessity for carrying a lighted match, which was

hazardous near gunpowder, and the glow and smoke prevented a surprise attack on either enemy or game. Nevertheless, its cheapness to produce and maintain enabled it to be the basic military arm in Europe for almost 250 years.

There are no known examples of matchlock pistols made in Europe during the fifteenth century, although matchlock pistols were made in considerable number in the Orient at a much later date. Early in the sixteenth century, the Japanese were introduced to the matchlock by Dutch and Portuguese traders, and this type of ignition system was the only type used in firearms made by the Japanese until 1860, at which time they converted to the percussion cap system.

The gun shown is a combination matchlock pistol and battle axe, illustrating the early pivoted serpentine. It was made in India during the latter part of the eighteenth century.

Shown below is a Japanese matchlock pistol made about 1800, and equipped with the more advanced trigger mechanism.

3 WHEEL LOCK

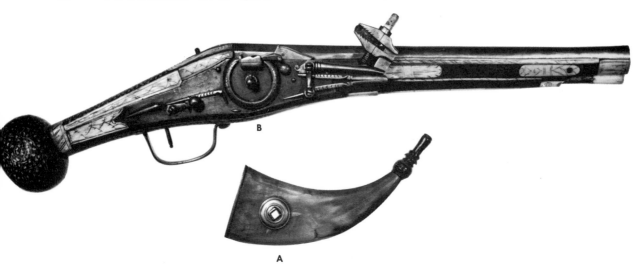

THE WHEEL LOCK was invented around 1500, and it is not certain whether it was of German or Italian origin. Most arms historians attribute the invention to Germany. This ignition system was a great improvement over the matchlock, since a gun could now be loaded, primed and subsequently fired on a moment's notice.

The wheel lock mechanism was made of relatively soft iron, and consequently one of the metallic sulfides called pyrites was used to generate ignition sparks in lieu of a piece of flint. The pyrites, however, was extremely friable and crumbled when pressed to the wheel. This resulted in clogging of the wheel housing.

There were some disadvantages as well as advantages connected with the wheel-lock. The fragile lock mechanism was very complicated, and therefore expensive to make and keep in good repair. As a result,

only the nobility and wealthier people of that era could afford to own a wheel lock. Also, if the spanner, used to wind the wheel, was lost, the wheel lock would be useless.

Since the wheel lock made the pistol practicable for the first time, the cavalry eventually adopted this weapon, and, as a result, made rapid changes in military tactics, especially in Germany and northern Europe.

The earliest known example of a wheel lock that can be dated is a combined crossbow and gun in the Bayerisches National Museum in Munich. This gun was made for Archduke Ferdinand of Austria between 1521 and 1526.

The specimen above is a Saxon wheel lock dag, with the date 1587 inscribed on the barrel. The combination spanner and powder flask also shown, in addition to holding the gunpowder, served as a tool for winding the mechanism.

[15]

4 SNAPHAUNCE

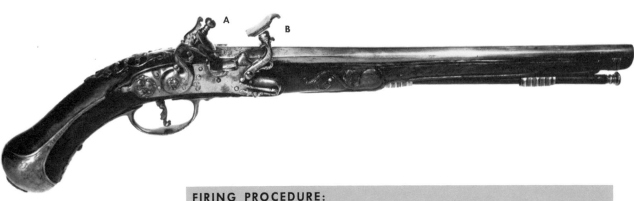

FIRING PROCEDURE:

1. Priming powder is placed in the pan, and the pan cover (a) is slid over top of pan to protect the powder.
2. When the trigger is pulled, the pan cover opens automatically and exposes priming powder in pan to the sparks generated by the flint striking the frizzen (b). Ignition of the priming powder penetrates barrel vent to set off main charge.

THE NAME SNAPHAUNCE is of Dutch origin, and means "snapping hen" or "pecking fowl." This term is descriptive of the action that snaps a piece of steel against a flint to produce sparks. The Snaphaunce appeared in the Netherlands about 1560 and was the first form of the flintlock ignition system.

The frizzen and pan cover on the Snaphaunce are two separate pieces. However, when the cock is released, a link arrangement causes the pan cover to uncover the flashpan and thereby expose the priming powder to the sparks that are generated. Since the flashpan cover and the frizzen, or battery, were separate pieces, no half-cock or safety position was provided. A few snaphaunce weapons were made in which it was necessary to uncover the flashpan manually.

Snaphaunce arms were not significantly an improvement in performance over the late period wheel locks. Their virtues lay mainly in their cheapness to produce, since a good snaphaunce cost only about one-fourth the price of a good wheel lock. Also, the snaphaunce did not need a separate spanner, which was used to wind the wheel lock mechanism. The snaphaunce reached the peak of its refinement in the sophisticated Italian gun of about 1630.

The specimen above is a fine quality snaphaunce pistol made in Brescia, Italy about 1665. Brescian pistols have attained a reputation of being among the finest firearms ever produced.

5 DOG LOCK

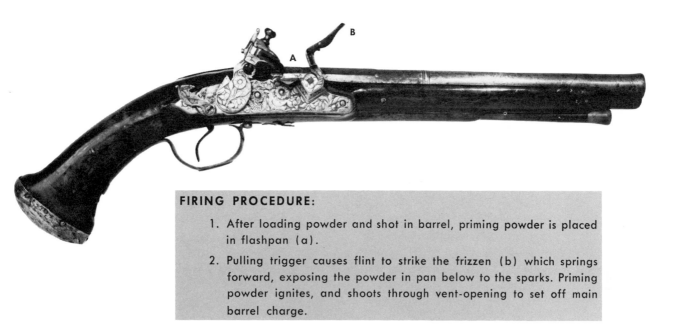

FIRING PROCEDURE:

1. After loading powder and shot in barrel, priming powder is placed in flashpan (a).

2. Pulling trigger causes flint to strike the frizzen (b) which springs forward, exposing the powder in pan below to the sparks. Priming powder ignites, and shoots through vent-opening to set off main barrel charge.

THE DOG LOCK, also called the English or Jacobean lock, followed the Miquelet and was the last of the flintlock family before the development of the true flintlock. The snaphaunce suffered from the fragility of its weak battery arm, and the Miquelet from the fragility of its exterior mainspring and slender-stemmed cock. What was required next was a combination of the best features of each: a gunlock with the durable inside workings of the snaphaunce and the efficient L-shaped one-piece flashpan cover of the Miquelet.

Between 1620 and 1630, English gunsmiths turned out firearms combining these features. Their work was so primitive, however, that it is necessary to make a distinction between them and what was later to be termed the "true flintlock," for which reason they have become known by the terms dog lock, English lock, or Jacobean flintlock. The term dog lock, though commonly used, is actually a misnomer. It is an English lock or Jacobean flintlock employing a "dog" behind the hammer to hold it at half-cock.

The specimen above is a typical massive English military Jacobean flintlock pistol of the English Civil War and Commonwealth Period (1642-1660) with a "dog" safety catch, made by Skinner.

6 MIQUELET LOCK

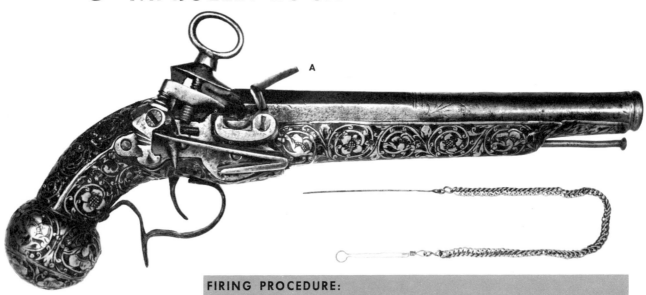

A

THE SPANISH, OR MIQUELET, lock had its origin in Spain about 1580. This lock was the last link between all earlier ignition systems and the true flintlock, which was to dominate firearms for two centuries from 1630 on.

For the first time, the battery was combined with the flashpan cover in one L-shaped piece, the upright section being struck by the flint and the horizontal forming the flashpan cover. The Miquelet also had a half-cock position for the hammer.

Miquelet lock guns lasted for some 250 years, and except for the British-made flintlock guns of the late eighteenth century they remain among the finest guns made until the introduction of the percussion system around 1830.

There was only one major variation of the Miquelet, which was the Italian Miquelet appearing in southern Italy about 1625. The difference lay mainly in a slight mechanical variation in the operation of the lock itself. However, the Spanish action was considered superior. In both instances, the mainspring was located on the exterior of the lock plate.

The Miquelet lock was originally known as the Spanish lock. During Wellington's campaign to drive Napoleon out of Spain, a band of Spanish soldiers of fortune, called "Miqueletes," were issued light-weight muskets equipped with the Spanish lock instead of the true flintlock. Thus the association was made by the French and British soldiers, who between 1805 and 1813 attached the term Miquelet to the gunlock itself, a term by which it has been known ever since.

The pistol shown above is a Spanish ball-butt, Miquelet lock, flint pistol made around 1690. The handle and forestock are completely covered in brass, which is deeply chiselled throughout. The pick shown below the pistol was used to unplug the vent-opening on flintlock pistols.

7 FLINTLOCK

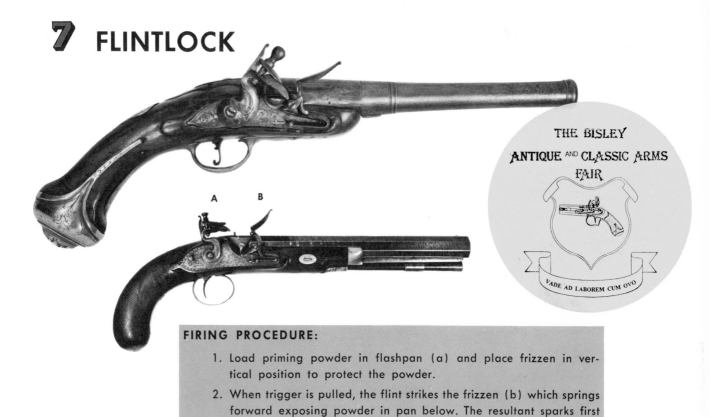

A   B

THE BISLEY
ANTIQUE AND CLASSIC ARMS
FAIR

VADE AD LABOREM CUM OVO

FIRING PROCEDURE:

1. Load priming powder in flashpan (a) and place frizzen in vertical position to protect the powder.

2. When trigger is pulled, the flint strikes the frizzen (b) which springs forward exposing powder in pan below. The resultant sparks first ignite the priming powder and then the main barrel charge.

THE FIRST TRUE FLINTLOCKS appeared in the vicinity of Paris around 1630. This weapon differed from the Miquelet lock and snaphaunce in that it employed a wholly interior mechanism and a one-piece L-shaped flashpan cover and battery, just as did the Jacobean flintlock. Beyond this, its distinctive features were those of refinement. The cock, or hammer, of the true flintlock was fashioned in the gooseneck shape in which it was to survive for two centuries, being later only made more elegant in the sweep of its proportions. The sear, rather than protruding through the lock plate to catch the rear of the cock, now was pivoted vertically on a horizontal screw and engaged successively two notches in the tumbler inside the lock. The first was the half-cock notch, or "half-bent." The second notch held the hammer at full cock, where it could be easily forced out by the trigger. From France, the new lock spread quickly throughout most of Western Europe. It never succeeded in replacing the Miquelet, but for the next two

hundred years it was virtually the standard lock for all of the better guns. The true flintlock proved much more reliable and faster than any gunlock known.

The ancestors of present-day Americans used flintlock arms under the British flag against the French and Indians, and against the British during the American Revolution and the War of 1812. Even today, the flintlock remains in use in regions where percussion caps and cartridges are scarce. Although the English makers' first attempts at the true flintlock were very crude, their workmanship later produced the finest flintlock arms in the world.

The specimen at the top was made by L. Annely about 1680 and has brass mountings and an unscrew type of barrel.

The pistol below is a flintlock dueller made in London about 1810 by Joseph Manton. This pistol represents the ultimate in the development of flintlock arms prior to their being made obsolete by the advent of the percussion ignition system.

8 DUAL IGNITION

Durong the early manufacture of percussion cap weapons in the 1820's, many sportsmen preferred flintlock guns to the early percussion guns. The reason for this preference was the belief that flint guns shot stronger, although the percussion cap guns shot quicker.

To satisfy those who were still a little dubious about giving up their tried and proven flintlocks in favor of the newfangled percussion ignition, some guns were made incorporating both systems. The flintlock and percussion ignition was not the first example of dual ignition since, previous to this, matchlock and wheel lock combinations were also produced.

It is not difficult to understand a shooter's reluctance to discard his flintlock gun if one stopped to realize that this practice of striking a piece of pyrite or flint against a steel had been used for over 300 years to discharge firearms.

A practical reason in favor of these dual ignition guns was the fact that they could still be fired after the supply of percussion caps had temporarily run out.

The pistol at the top, combining both flint and percussion ignition was made in London by Ezekiel Baker, and the date 1821 is engraved on the lock plate. Baker and another London gunmaker named S. Davis were the only ones who ever produced more than just a few examples of these dual ignition guns. It is worth mentioning that the Davis lock of 1822 was the first percussion cap lock to be pictured in an English patent. Although the Baker lock is dated a year earlier, it evidently was not patented.

The derringer pistol below is also dual ignition, except that in this case the percussion cap is combined with the metallic cartridge. This pistol is marked on the top of the barrel "Williamson's Pat. Oct. 2, 1866, New York." By pressing the catch located just forward of the trigger guard, the barrel slides forward for loading. The reloadable auxiliary percussion chamber pictured above was furnished with the derringer. Consequently, if no .41 caliber rim-fire cartridges were available, this chamber could be loaded with powder and bullet, fitted with a percussion cap, and inserted in the barrel. The hammer was constructed with two spurs to fire whichever type ammunition was being used at the time, "Wild Bill" Hickok was reputed to have carried one of these derringers.

9 FULMINATE POWDER

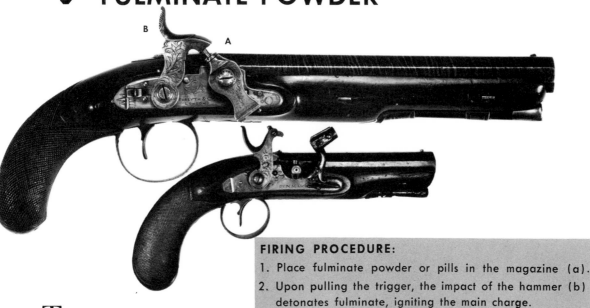

FIRING PROCEDURE:
1. Place fulminate powder or pills in the magazine (a).
2. Upon pulling the trigger, the impact of the hammer (b) detonates fulminate, igniting the main charge.

THE INVENTOR OF RECORD for the percussion ignition system was the Reverend Alexander John Forsyth of Belhelvie, Scotland, according to patent office records dated April 11, 1807. This invention revolutionized firearms, and is generally considered to have been the greatest in the history of firearms. Unfortunately, as so often happens, Reverend Forsyth died before his contribution received the recognition that it deserved.

Reverend Forsyth's patent dealt with the ignition of gunpowder through the use of a fulminate. Fulminates are salts, formed by the dissolution of metals and acids, which will explode violently when struck. The properties of fulminates were known as early as the seventeenth century, but it was not until after 1800 that successful experiments were carried out in connection with firearms. With this invention, the basis for the modern metallic cartridge was laid.

At first, fulminate powder was placed in a magazine, and from this magazine the powder was loaded into a covered flashpan. Later, the fulminate mixture was formed into pills, or pellets. In both cases, however, the firearm was fired by the hammer striking the fulminate powder.

In 1842, Reverend Forsyth received a reward of 200 pounds from his government. A few months after his death in 1843, an additional 1000 pounds was distributed among his relatives. Public interest ended after these monetary awards until 1929, when a few historians, collectors, and sportsmen erected a bronze tablet in his honor in the Tower of London.

The specimen at the top is a scent bottle-type percussion pistol, made by Forsyth & Co. in London about 1810, which employed loose fulminate powder. The name "scent bottle" is derived from the resemblance of the magazine to a perfume bottle of that period. This pistol was the first type of gun to use the percussion system of ignition.

The specimen below also employs loose fulminate powder for ignition. To prepare for firing, the magazine, filled with fulminate, is brought down so that it rests on top of the flashpan. An opening in the bottom of the magazine aligns itself with a cavity in the pan, and the downward movement of the magazine causes a sliding plate to uncover the opening to permit the cavity to fill with powder. The front nose of the hammer, in descending, knocks the magazine clear of the pan, and strikes the fulminate. As the magazine is knocked back, the sliding plate covers the opening to prevent spillage.

[21]

10 PILL OR PELLET LOCK

FIRING PROCEDURE:

1. Place pellet in hollow plug (a) and insert floating firing pin.
2. When plug falls on anvil (b), the firing pin crushes the pellet and the resultant flame then ignites the powder charge in the barrel.

From the time of Forsyth's invention of the percussion system of ignition in 1807, and before the copper percussion cap was invented, four different types of percussion ignitions were in use. These early percussion firearms were detonated by loose fulminate powder, fulminate wax or varnish-coated pellets or pills, fulminate in metal tubes, and fulminate sandwiched between paper patches.

The least successful of the four listed above was the pellet. It consisted of powder rolled into a small "pill," and coated with wax or varnish. The first pellet lock was patented in London in 1816 by Joseph Manton, and guns equipped with this type of lock were the first that he produced operating on the percussion ignition system. These locks were so constructed as to be interchangeable with contemporary flintlocks.

Examples of these locks are extremely rare for two reasons, the first being that Forsyth brought a suit for patent infringement against Manton and was successful. The second reason was that in general the locks were not well-received by the public, and most of the guns having them were later converted to percussion cap.

The detachable plugs or striker heads were carried in a small case, which had a wooden insert containing 24 holes to accommodate the plugs. They were loaded by the shooter in advance, and it was necessary to affix a loaded plug to the hammer for each firing. The plug had a hole drilled through its entire length which narrowed at the end that made contact with the anvil or nipple affixed to the breech end of the barrel. A pellet was dropped into this hole, followed by the firing pin.

The specimen at the top is a scent bottle-type, double-barrel pistol made by W. Green in London about 1825. It is not certain whether this pistol had its magazines filled with fulminate in the forms of loose powder, or in small pellets, since some makers were not too specific as to which should be used.

The pistol below is an American pill lock pistol made by Rogers and Heart, Utica, New York.

The detached pellet lock shown is a Joseph Manton 1816 lock, and is probably one of only two such locks known to be in existence.

The brass dispenser shown was made by Charles Moore. It has a simple ratchet wheel which feeds one pellet at a time through the small tubular muzzle.

11 TUBE LOCK

In 1816, the famous English gunmaker, Joseph Manton, known to sportsmen of his day as the "king of the gunsmiths," patented his first percussion lock, which was known as the pellet lock. Two years later, in 1818, he patented his famous tube lock. This system employed the use of a copper tube 5/8″ long and about 1/16″ in diameter which was open at both ends. The tube was filled with percussion powder and then inserted in the touchhole, or vent. The protruding part rested on a small anvil which was an integral part of the lock plate. The hammer striking the tube crimped shut the protruding end, and the fire shot forward to ignite the propellant charge in the barrel. A snap cover was let down to secure the tube. This system worked very well. Its only drawback was that a tiny jet of fire issued from the outer end of the tube in spite of the fact that the blow of the striker crimped the tube shut, and at times a few sparks blew into the shooter's face. Also, the ex-

plosion occasionally discharged the tube from the vent with enough force to possibly injure a bystander.

Tube locks were made by a number of European makers, and the shape of the tube primers varied somewhat. The only American tube lock was designed by E. J. Gerdon in 1860, and there is only one known surviving example of his gun.

While the tube lock ignition system was, next to the copper cap, the most popular system in Europe, it did not enjoy as great a popularity in America.

The specimen at the top is a tube lock pistol made by Joseph Manton, and several Manton tube detonators are pictured with the pistol.

The specimen below is a breech-loading pistol made by H. Tanner in Paris about 1840. In this instance, an unconventional-type tube is inserted in the opening, where it is struck on its end by the side-acting hammer.

12 PATCH LOCK

THE PATCH LOCK was another of the experimental systems prior to the invention of the percussion cap, and history leaves us guessing as to its inventor. The patch priming consisted of fulminate placed between pieces of paper and sealed by a coat of varnish. They were similar in appearance to the caps used in children's toy pistols. These patches were pressed into a slight cavity in the striker head, and were detonated when the striker hit the nipple. In early patch lock weapons, the nipples were an integral part of the barrel. Since fulminate powder is highly corrosive, it was often necessary to replace the nipples, and as a result, nipples for later patch lock firearms were made with a threaded screw base for easy replacement.

Patch lock guns had easily detachable striker heads, just as did the pellet locks. These striker heads were also loaded in advance, and a supply was always carried by the shooter. They were solid, as compared with the hollowed-out strikers of the pellet lock.

Fulminate in loose powder form, pellets, or paper patches were referred to as "primings." Fulminate in variously shaped metal tubes were called "primers."

No patch lock guns were ever produced in America. However, prior to 1830 punch locks, later called pill locks, were produced in the western part of New York State. These guns were detonated by a fulminate pill, as were their European counterparts.

The specimen above is one of a cased pair of engraved patch lock traveling pistols made by Samuel Nock, Regent Circus, London, around 1825. This set is one of only three such cased pairs known to exist.

Also shown is a wooden block from the cased set containing 24 patch lock striker heads, together with a few of the individual paper patches.

13 PERCUSSION CAP

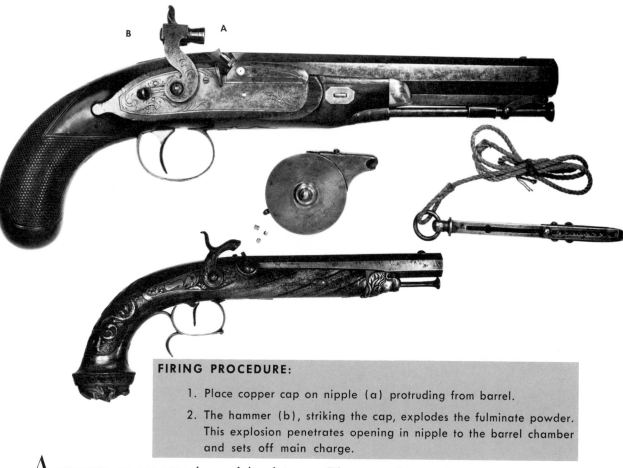

B · A

FIRING PROCEDURE:

1. Place copper cap on nipple (a) protruding from barrel.

2. The hammer (b), striking the cap, explodes the fulminate powder. This explosion penetrates opening in nipple to the barrel chamber and sets off main charge.

A NUMBER OF PERSONS have claimed to be the inventor of the percussion cap. The United States issued a patent for the copper percussion cap to Joshua Shaw on June 19, 1822. Shaw was an English artist who came to this country in 1817 and settled in Philadelphia.

In granting this patent, the U. S. Patent Office overlooked a previous patent for a percussion cap that was taken out in France on July 29, 1818, by a man named Prelat. The earliest English patent for a percussion cap was obtained in 1822.

It is not likely that Prelat was the true inventor of the copper cap, since he frequently imported guns from England and proceeded to secure French patents for any new features. In summary, it appears that the copper cap was first patented in France by Prelat. As to who was the first to experimentally place a metal cap on a nipple, probably no one will ever know.

The percussion cap firearm came into general use about 1835, and was adopted by American and European armies in 1840. Many flintlock mechanisms were altered to the percussion system by replacing hammer and inserting a nipple assembly in the barrel.

The early percussion pistol at the top was made in England about 1825 by Jackson, and the hammer is equipped with a replaceable striking nose. This pistol also has a vent below the nipple to permit gas escape. However, vents were eliminated by 1830 because the gunmakers came to realize that the use of a vent, while it reduced the kick, also reduced the power of the charge.

The pistol below is of the later conventional type of percussion cap pistol having a one-piece hammer. It is one of a very ornate pair of duelling or target pistols, made by G. Micheloni in Brescia, Italy about 1835. Two types of cappers used to dispense percussion caps are also shown.

14 TAPE PRIMER

THE BEST KNOWN and most successful tape primer was invented in 1845 by a dentist, Dr. Edward Maynard, living in Washington, D.C. There are two types of Maynard tape primer locks. One feeds the individual primers by means of "fingers," the other by means of a "feeding wheel."

Maynard submitted his first tape primer to the United States Government Board at West Point on January 29, 1845. His first proposition to the U.S. was to utilize the tape primer in connection with the alteration of thousands of flintlock muskets then on hand. The original percussion cone, or nipple, did not accommodate the use of a regular percussion cap. This, however, was changed at the suggestion of the board of Army officers soon afterward. Between 1845 and 1854, Dr. Maynard received $76,000 from the U.S. Government for the use of his invention.

The roll of Maynard tape primers is made of two narrow strips of paper cemented together and enclosing fifty mounds of a fulminating mixture, all of which are separated. In firing, when the hammer is pulled back, the feed mechanism pushes a section of tape containing a cap over the nipple. When the hammer falls, it simultaneously cuts off a section of tape and explodes the primer, which in turn fires the barrel charge.

Percussion weapons with the tape primer device were popular with cavalry soldiers because they eliminated the difficult operation, while on horseback, of placing a percussion cap on a gun nipple.

The specimen above is a Massachusetts Arms Co. revolver with a tape primer mechanism. Actually, it is quite similar in operation to a toy cap pistol. Shown with the revolver is a tin container holding ten rolls of tape primers. One roll of the primers is shown wrapped in waterproof paper as it comes from the can. On the other roll, the paper has been removed.

15 DISC PRIMER

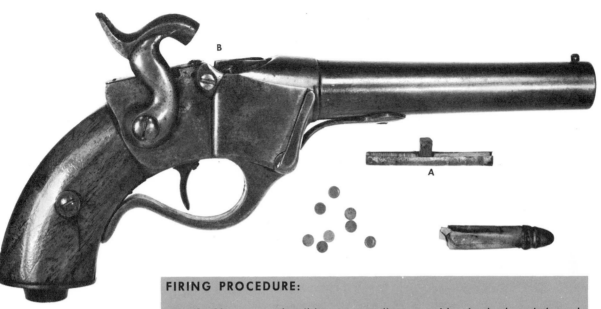

On October 5, 1852, Christian Sharps patented his disc primer device. The operation is as follows: A charger, as shown above, containing 25 wafer-shaped disc primers, is inserted into a vertical primer magazine located behind the percussion nipple. Cocking the hammer causes a sliding part, called a driver, to be forced back. When the hammer falls, the driver springs forward to push one disc out toward the nipple. The descending hammer catches the flying disc and detonates it on the nipple below. Mr. Sharps pointed out in his patent that it was necessary for the driver to toss the disc into the air with just enough force so that it would neither fall short of nor overshoot the nipple.

On April 12, 1859, Richard Lawrence patented an improvement on the Sharps disc primer called the "Lawrence cutoff." This cutoff enabled the primer feed to be disengaged, and thereby allowed the use of copper caps. The 1852 and 1853 Sharps guns were not equipped with the Lawrence cutoff, but the 1859 and 1863 models did have this improvement.

In 1859, Jesse S. Butterfield also patented a disc primer mechanism. In this instance, however, the disc was conducted to the nipple, rather than being thrown toward the nipple as in the Sharps guns. The disc primer is about $\frac{1}{8}''$ in diameter, and is made of two circular halves, turned up at right angles with the fulminate compressed between the two halves.

The specimen above is a Sharps breech-loading disc primer percussion pistol made about 1860, and, like all Sharps guns, fires a combustible cartridge. The cartridge is breechloaded by lowering the trigger guard, which in turn opens the breechblock. Shown with the pistol is a brass charger loaded with twenty-five $\frac{1}{8}''$ diameter disc primers. Alongside are a group of the primers which have been emptied from a charger.

16 1st SELF-CONTAINED CARTRIDGE

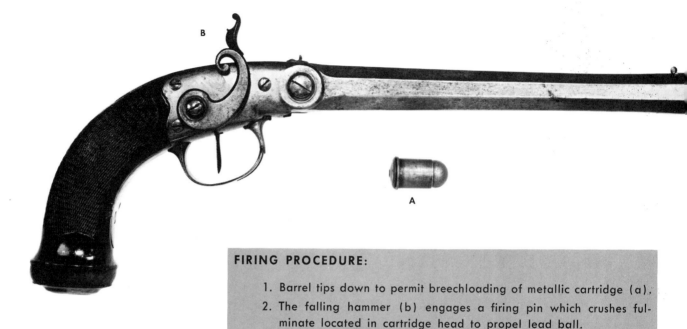

FIRING PROCEDURE:

1. Barrel tips down to permit breechloading of metallic cartridge (a).
2. The falling hammer (b) engages a firing pin which crushes fulminate located in cartridge head to propel lead ball.

ON SEPTEMBER 29, 1812, Jean Samuel Pauly, a Swiss living in Paris, secured a French patent for a breech-loading gun that fired the first self-contained, rimmed, reloadable, center-fire cartridge. Pauly's gun was also the first breechloader to use any form of percussion ignition.

The cartridge used for the Pauly pistols consisted of a relatively thick reloadable brass cartridge case, as shown above. In the center of the cartridge head is a ⅛″ diameter recess where the priming is placed. A small hole is located in the center of the recess to admit the ignition flash. The cartridges used in Pauly shotguns and rifles consisted of a brass rosette, or disc, similar to the cartridge head of the pistol cartridge. This rosette has an integral screw on one side which engages the cardboard end of a paper cartridge case. A round lead ball was squeezed into the open end of both the pistol brass cartridge case and the shotgun and rifle paper cartridge case. In the

section of this book devoted to cartridges, there can be seen photographs illustrating the making of a Pauly paper cartridge with rosette base, together with a set of tools used to make these cartridges.

Pauly firearms were reliable, efficient, and could be fired about as fast as any modern single-shot pistol. In spite of these advantages, the French Ministry of War rejected the Pauly firearms for military use on the grounds of high cost, fragility, and the danger of getting the propellant and ignition powders reversed while fighting under fire on the battlefield.

Pauly can be credited with many other firearm inventions that were well ahead of their time. The exact date of his death is not known, but it is thought to have been some time prior to 1828.

The specimen above is a Pauly pistol, circa 1812, which fired the first self-contained center-fire cartridge. The cartridge fired in this pistol is also shown.

[28]

17 NEEDLE FIRE

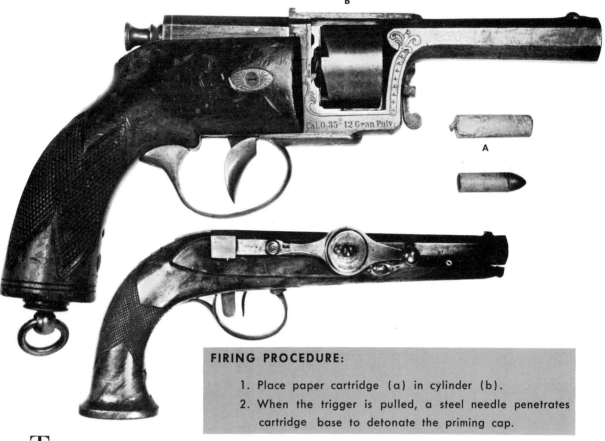

FIRING PROCEDURE:

1. Place paper cartridge (a) in cylinder (b).
2. When the trigger is pulled, a steel needle penetrates cartridge base to detonate the priming cap.

THE NEEDLE GUN was developed by Johann Nikolaus von Dreyse in 1829. Dreyse served an apprenticeship in Paris from 1808 to 1814 under the famous gunmaker Pauly, who patented the first self-contained cartridge. At the end of this training period, Dreyse apparently returned to Germany when Pauly went to England.

The cartridges used in a needle gun are usually paper covered, but in a few instances some were covered in cloth. At the base of the bullet is a cardboard wad, or sabot, into which a fulminate primer is placed. In the true needle gun, the primer is sandwiched between the bullet and powder charge. The reason the Germans located the primer in front of the powder charge was because they believed that greater power could be developed by igniting the gunpowder at the front of the charge, and consequently have it burn backwards. Recent tests in this country have verified the accuracy of this theory.

Although this method of ignition resulted in about ten percent higher bullet velocity, it was also coupled with a weakness. The steel needles, being imbedded in the powder charge at the time of the explosion, could not withstand this intense heat and thereby became brittle, necessitating frequent replacement.

The needle-fire system saw its greatest use in the Dreyse 1841 model breech-loading rifle, which was adopted in 1848 as the official rifle of the German Army. The weapon was the predecessor of all bolt-action rifles, and gave Germany many military victories in Europe during the second half of the nineteenth century.

The specimen above is a rare double-action, needle-fire revolver made by Dreyse.

Below is a rare muzzle-loading needle-fire pistol made by Dreyse and Collenbusch.

18 PIN-FIRE

FIRING PROCEDURE:

1. Load cartridge in cylinder so that the pin (a) protrudes through notch provided.
2. The hammer (b) strikes pin, which in turn crushes priming pellet, located inside cartridge case, to fire bullet.

A FRENCHMAN, M. LEFAUCHEUX, designed a pin-fire self-contained cartridge about 1836 which could be breechloaded and fired with a conventional-type hammer mechanism. The cartridge consisted of a metal base with cardboard tube, similar to an empty shotgun shell. The detonating pellet was placed inside the base, and a pin, with its inner end resting against the pellet, penetrated the wall of the cartridge. The breech chambers of pin-fire firearms are notched to accommodate the pins of the cartridge. Consequently, the hammer striking the pin crushes it against the priming pellet to detonate the cartridge.

In 1846, another Frenchman, M. Houllier, patented a pin-fire cartridge which had a copper case. This metallic cartridge case was a great improvement over the cardboard case previously devised by Lefaucheux, since the copper expanded against the chamber wall and effectively sealed the breech against any gas escape. After the explosion, the case contracted sufficiently to be easily ejected from the chamber.

In addition to being complicated and expensive to manufacture, the greatest drawback to pin-fire cartridges was their susceptibility to accidental firing as a result of careless handling.

The specimen above is a Lefaucheux seven-shot pin-fire revolver of the type that was imported from France and used by both Confederate and Union forces during the Civil War. Pictured with the revolver is a pin-fire cartridge that was used in these guns.

19 VOLCANIC

FIRING PROCEDURE:

1. Load conical shaped lead cartridge (a), which is hollowed out to house powder and percussion cap, into magazine located underneath barrel.

2. The hammer (b) engages a firing pin which strikes primer located in base of cartridge.

VOLCANIC ARMS were manufactured first by Smith & Wesson in Norwich, Connecticut, then by Volcanic Repeating Arms Co. in New Haven, and by the New Haven Arms Co. of the same city, during the period 1854-1860.

Forerunners to the Volcanics were the Hunt and Jennings rifles; however, there was only one experimental model made of the Hunt gun. The cartridge used in these guns was a lead ball, commonly referred to as a "rocket ball," with its hollow interior filled with gunpowder. It depended on outside priming for ignition. Although the Volcanic cartridge has a hollow cavity for gunpowder, it also contains its own primer, which is sandwiched between a cork and metal disc located at its base. The Hunt, Jennings, and Volcanic were all equipped with a cartridge magazine located under the barrel.

The Volcanics were of excellent design and were the forerunners of the famed Winchester repeating action. However, the am-

munition could not possibly hold a charge of powder suitable to produce high velocity and penetrating power. This fault caused these weapons to be redesigned in 1860 and patented under the name Henry Rifle. The ammunition used was a .44 caliber rim-fire metallic cartridge. Later modification of this same repeater principle developed into the famous Winchester 1866 and 1873 repeaters, the latter of which fired the famed .44 caliber center-fire metallic cartridge.

The pistol at the top is a .41 caliber, steel frame Smith & Wesson Repeating Pistol, long model, with 8″ barrel, made at Norwich, Connecticut in 1854 and marked with serial number 23. This was the first American pistol to fire fixed ammunition in which the bullet, propellant, and primer were all combined in one unit.

The specimen below is an engraved bronze frame Volcanic with six-inch barrel and ivory grips, made about 1856. Volcanic cartridges fired in this pistol are also pictured.

20 B-B CAP

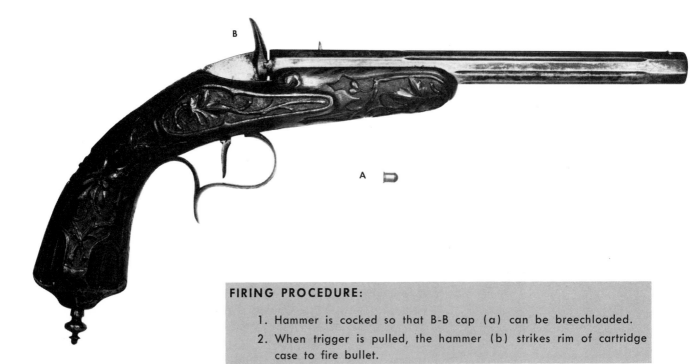

FIRING PROCEDURE:

1. Hammer is cocked so that B-B cap (a) can be breechloaded.
2. When trigger is pulled, the hammer (b) strikes rim of cartridge case to fire bullet.

DUELLING was popular in Europe during the first half of the nineteenth century, and consequently there were a number of shooting galleries around where men could shoot in an effort to improve their marksmanship. These galleries were called saloons in England and salons in France. A Frenchman, M. Flobert, conducted such a salon in Paris and, from the standpoint of improving business, he was looking for a fast and efficient way to load small caliber target pistols.

About 1845, Flobert invented what he called a B-B, or bullet-breach, cap. This consisted of pressing a small round lead ball into the open end of an oversized copper percussion cap, which was .22 caliber in size. The cap had a flanged rim so that it could seat itself properly in the barrel, and only

fulminate of mercury was used for both ignition and propellant.

The B-B caps had the necessary potency required for indoor gallery shooting, despite the fact that they were not loaded with any black gunpowder for bullet propulsion.

In the United States, Smith & Wesson improved the B-B cap by elongating the cartridge case and adding a black powder charge to give their first .22 caliber rim-fire metallic cartridge the power that was so badly lacking in the B-B cap. For this reason, the B-B cap is considered the granddaddy of modern rim-fire cartridges.

The specimen above is a single-shot .22 caliber pistol of the type that was used in European shooting galleries. Also shown is the B-B cap that was fired in these pistols.

21 METALLIC CARTRIDGE

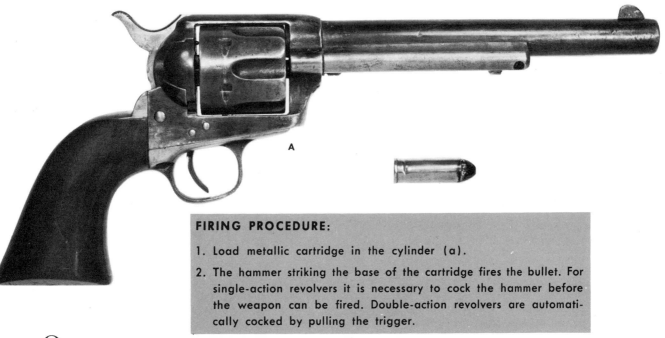

A

FIRING PROCEDURE:

1. Load metallic cartridge in the cylinder (a).
2. The hammer striking the base of the cartridge fires the bullet. For single-action revolvers it is necessary to cock the hammer before the weapon can be fired. Double-action revolvers are automatically cocked by pulling the trigger.

On APRIL 3, 1855, Rollin White of Hartford, Connecticut was granted United States patents for what he claimed were "new and useful improvements in repeating firearms." His invention was unsuccessful, and had it not been for one claim in the patent specification which called for "extending the chambers through the rear of the cylinder for the purpose of loading them at the breech from behind," no one would have had any interest whatsoever in White's patent.

About this same time, Horace Smith and Daniel Wesson had developed the first fully practical rim-fire cartridge from the Flobert bulleted breech cap, which in turn was little more than a rimmed percussion cap containing only fulminate powder. They were about ready to market a revolver with bored-through cylinder chambers to shoot this cartridge, when they learned from the patent office that the bored-through cylinder feature had already been patented by White. They immediately contacted him, and agreed to

manufacture revolvers under the latter's patent on a royalty basis.

About ten or twelve types of cartridge revolvers were made which legally circumvented the White patent. There were also a number manufactured which were clearly in violation of the patent. Within a week after the patent expired, a bill to permit a seven-year extension of White's 14-year rights was passed by both houses of Congress, without debate. President Grant returned the bill to the Senate without approval and stated ".... the government suffered inconvenience and embarrassment enough during the war in consequence of the inability of manufacturers to use the patent...." The bill was not passed over the Presidential veto.

The specimen above is a Colt black-powder, single-action .45 caliber revolver commonly called the Peacemaker. This model was brought out in 1872 following expiration of the Smith & Wesson patent. The cartridge used in this pistol is also shown.

[33]

22 AUTOMATIC

SYSTEM BORCHARDT PATENT.
DEUTSCHE WAFFEN-UND MUNITIONSFABRIKEN.
BERLIN.

FIRING PROCEDURE:

1. Insert magazine clip containing cartridges into handle.
2. When trigger is pulled, the resulting recoil ejects empty rimless cartridge case, and also strips a cartridge from magazine and places it in firing position.

THE FIRST TRUE AUTOMATIC, or self-loading pistol was the Borchardt 7.65 millimeter, which was manufactured in Germany by the Loewe Armsmaking Company of Berlin. This pistol, invented by a man named Borchardt who lived in Connecticut, was offered to the public in 1893. There were several automatic pistols introduced the year prior to the Borchardt, but these were manufactured in very small quantity and did not receive much publicity.

Although the Borchardt had several features which have become standard on modern automatic pistols, it still was not entirely satisfactory in its original form. As a result, around 1900 the weapon was redesigned by Georg Luger and manufactured by the Deutsche Waffen und Munitions Fabriken of Germany, and renamed the Luger, or parabellum as it is called in Europe.

Almost all small arms, although termed automatics, are actually semi-automatic in operation, since the trigger must be pulled to fire each shot. Machine guns, on the other hand, are fully automatic in that they will fire continuously whenever the trigger is pulled back, thus the machine gun is both self-firing and autoloading, whereas pistols are generally only autoloading. There were, however, several types of automatic pistols manufactured which were fully automatic in operation.

In 1885, Paul M. E. Vieille of France developed smokeless powder, which consisted of nitrocellulose reduced with solvents. Smokeless powder imparts greater velocity to the bullet by means of low pressure being applied through a longer space of time. It also has less jarring recoil and, as a result, smokeless powder is almost always used in the ammunition for automatic weapons.

The specimen above is a Borchardt 7.65 millimeter automatic pistol. This was the world's first automatic pistol to be made in any appreciable quantity and offered for sale. Pictured below is a wooden shoulder stock. The leather piece attached to the stock, together with the shoulder strap, converts the stock into a holster for the automatic.

PART II

Evolution of Air Guns

The development of the air gun is shown through its basic types, beginning with the blowgun and continuing up to the air guns of today.

Following the story of the development are other air guns that show the many varieties of types there were in each of the basic categories.

EVOLUTION OF AIR GUNS

1. BLOW GUN	
2. BELLOWS	
3. PNEUMATIC	
4. SPRING-CRANK	
5. SPRING	
6. FIRST GAS (CO₂)	
7. MODERN	

THE EARLIEST DOCUMENTED mention of a weapon using air as a motive power refers to Ctesibius, a Greek living in Alexandria in the second century B.C. He used the principle of the condensing syringe to achieve greater power of thrust for the huge stone-throwing machines used as war weapons by the Greeks. A cylinder was placed at each end of the machine, into which pistons were fitted. When a projectile was in place ready for firing, its weight depressed the pistons, which in turn compressed the air in the cylinders. When the machine was triggered, the pistons were forced upward, forcing the launching rope against the projectile with about three times the amount of thrust possible with a mechanical hurler.

The first recorded evidence of the invention of a mechanical air gun as a small arm to be carried by a man states that Hans Lobsinger, of Nuremberg, Germany invented an air rifle about 1560. No details were given as to the construction of this weapon, but since Lobsinger had invented an improved form of bellows, it is quite likely that this first air rifle could have operated on the bellows principle. While the invention of a mechanical air gun was not recorded until 1560, the blowgun, or blowpipe, was in use in medieval Europe and other parts of the world prior to that time.

It is difficult to understand why the air gun never achieved a great degree of popularity, despite its obvious advantages over the matchlock, wheel lock, and the various forms of the flintlock. The fact that it did not depend upon a spark or flame for ignition meant that it could be operated in any type of weather, whereas wind and rain severely hampered hunting and military operations when powder ignition systems were used. Its lack of smoke and comparative noiselessness, gave an element of surprise, of great advantage to the military. The air gun also lent itself more readily to rapid fire and repeating mechanisms than did firearms. This is obvious when one considers the great possibility of chain reaction and explosion due to the use of loose powder in firearms. Other advantages of air guns were the absence of barrel fouling, and the fact that little or no cleaning was required.

The major disadvantages of air guns are their expense of manufacture, as well as high maintenance costs due to their intricate construction. In the case of pneumatic weapons, there is also the attendant danger of an accidental explosion because of the air being under compression. Because of their noiseless discharge, air guns were often considered the weapons of poachers and assassins and were outlawed from time to time in various countries.

Although there have been many variations of air guns, the following pages illustrate the fundamental types of air-powered weapons.

1 BLOWGUN

THE SIMPLEST FORM of an air weapon is the blowgun. It is impossible to trace its exact origin, as it was probably developed more or less independently in many parts of the world. While it is commonly thought of as being the weapon of primitive tribes and cultures, there is evidence to show that it was used in Europe in the fifteenth century, and possibly earlier. Leonardo da Vinci mentions a blowgun in some of his notebooks. It was common in Southeast Asia and South America, and was used by the Cherokee Indians of North America.

The South American Indians of the Orinoco and Amazon Basins have probably made the greatest use of a blowgun as a hunting weapon, and it is still widely used there today. According to W. M. Stirling in his report on the Jivaro Indians of the upper Amazon River, no mention can be found of the blowgun before the seventeenth century. He thinks it likely that Spanish galleons, sailing across the Pacific in the sixteenth century, carried natives of Southeast Asia, possibly the Philippines, who escaped into the South American jungles and introduced the use of the blowgun.

The blowgun was and is primarily a weapon for shooting game, and was not used in warfare. The Jivaros believe that it would bring bad luck to use it against man. It varies in length from two feet to twenty feet, the usual being from six to ten feet. There are several methods employed in the making of a blowgun, the simplest form being a hollowed-out reed. Some consist of a hollow reed placed between two pieces of grooved-out wood, which are then bound together with fibers, and some tribes of Borneo even bored their blow guns out of a single piece of wood. The range depends upon the length of the gun and the blowing ability of the user. The longer ones were usually efficient up to 60 yards, and their range has been recorded as far as 100 yards.

The darts are first sharpened and then dipped in poison, as poison was necessary to make their use effective except on small birds. Snake venom and poisonous plants were used, the best known being curare from the wourali vine in South America. This poison paralyzes the motor nerves causing death by suffocation. Curare does not contaminate the flesh of the game, it being necessary to remove only the small portion surrounding the dart. When firing at monkeys, the hunter would first partly cut through the tip end of the dart. This was done to cause the poison tip to break off when the monkey attempted to pull the dart from the wound.

The blowgun above is from Ecuador, and its length indicates that it was probably made for a young boy, or for ceremonial uses. Also shown is a quiver complete with darts, and a gourd containing tree cotton. This cotton is wrapped around one tip of the dart to obtain a close fit in the blowgun.

[39]

2 BELLOWS

FROM ALL INFORMATION AVAILABLE, it seems most probable that the bellows-type of air gun was first made in Germany in the sixteenth century. Although there are no existing specimens of this early period available for examination, it is a recorded fact that Hans Lobsinger of Nuremberg, Germany invented an air rifle about 1560. Lobsinger was a noted mechanic, and records show that he had previously invented an improved form of bellows. In view of this, it appears highly probable that the first mechanical air gun operated on the bellows principle.

Bellows guns have a hollowed-out stock in which the bellows and necessary operating mechanism are housed. When the gun is cocked, the bellows is held open by means of one or two V-springs. Pressing the trigger releases the spring, causing the bellows to compress suddenly. The resulting rush of air discharges the bullet from the barrel.

The bellows gun and the sixteenth century wheel lock have certain characteristics in common, both in outward appearance and operation of the mechanism. Both of these types are cocked by means of a spanner or winding crank. On the bellows gun, a square male shaft located at the butt end of the stock was wound by means of a crank or lever. This is another factor which points up the likelihood that the bellows gun was the earliest form of mechanical air weapon.

The bellows guns were the weakest of all the types of air guns, and were used principally for target work and indoor shooting. The most popular form that was manufactured was the German Bolzenbuchse, which means literally "dart gun." These guns were ornate and expensive to make. They were unbelievably accurate at a range of about forty feet, and are probably the most accurate ever used for target shooting. The darts which they shot were specially made, and so accurate that shooters carefully pulled hairs from the tail of the dart to make for a truer shot.

It is unfortunate that there are no sixteenth century bellows guns available for study. No existing specimens have been authenticated as being made earlier than the late eighteenth century. The best known early American air gun was that mentioned many times in the Journal of the Lewis and Clark expedition of 1804-1806. While this is believed to be a bellows-type gun, the wording of the Journal does not make this clear.

The bellows pistol shown is a German make dating in the latter part of the eighteenth century, and the barrel tips up at the breech for loading. Practically all arms operating on the bellows principle are long guns, and pistols are extremely rare.

3 PNEUMATIC

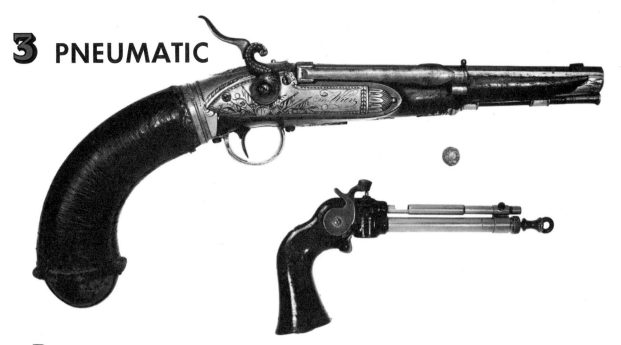

Pneumatic guns are the most powerful of all air guns, and receive their power from compressed air in a reservoir. The earliest mention of this type is to be found in a treatise published in Paris in 1644 by M. Mersenne. According to this treatise, Marin Bourgeois of Lisieux in Normandy made an air rifle for King Henry IV of Navarre, who reigned from 1589 to 1610, but details of this piece are lacking. The earliest documentation for a pneumatic gun credits its design to Otto von Guericke of Magdeburg, Germany around 1640. He also perfected an efficient air pump.

The only country to make any appreciable use of the air gun as a weapon of war was Austria. In 1790, the Austrian army trained a special air rifle corps of about 1300 men armed with a repeating air rifle designed by M. Girardoni. The stocks of these guns were detachable and contained enough compressed air for about 20 to 25 shots. The soldier carried into battle with him two to four air flasks, and carts carrying extra flasks and air pumps supported each company. The effectiveness of these weapons was such that Napoleon ordered the execution of any Austrian found carrying an air gun.

Many air rifles were constructed on the pneumatic principle in the eighteenth and nineteenth centuries, and these are of three basic types. Some had detachable stocks which contained metal reservoirs, and these were pumped up to pressures sometimes as much as 550 lbs. The average pumped-up reservoir contained enough compressed air for 10 to 20 shots. Another type was very similar to that described above, except that the air was contained in a detachable metal ball which usually screwed onto the underside of the gun. Less common than the two types above was an air rifle having the reservoir for the air in the form of a jacket around the outside of the barrel.

Pneumatic arms had two advantages in particular over the spring types, as they were capable of higher velocities and had very little recoil, which made for greater accuracy.

The pistol at the top is an engraved air pistol with the air reservoir located in the leather-covered butt. This piece was made by the famous maker Girardoni in Vienna around 1770.

The gun below was patented by E. H. Hawley of Kalamazoo, Michigan in 1869. This type was probably the first successful American compressed air arm to be produced. Here the pump is located underneath the barrel, and it is necessary to operate the pump separately for each shot.

4 SPRING-CRANK

THIS TYPE OF AIR GUN employed a detachable crank, used to extend or compress the springs which are attached to a piston operating in the air cylinder. It was usually necessary to make from ½ to 2½ turns of the crank to cock the weapon. When the trigger is pulled, the springs cause the piston to be driven forward with considerable force in the air cylinder. The close-fitting piston compresses the air in the cylinder which escapes through a small vent adjacent to the bullet chamber, forcing the bullet out of the barrel.

It is not known when the crank system originated. Most of these guns were breech-loaders, although some few muzzle-loaders were made. The American crank-operated gallery gun was manufactured by a number of American gunsmiths in the third quarter of the nineteenth century. Many of these makers did not mark their guns with their names, possibly because of patent infringement, or because they were simply copying German types brought here from the old country. In the period immediately following the Civil War, gallery shooting was a popular sport in city areas, and it was during this period that these guns enjoyed their greatest use. The cost of such a gun was in the neighborhood of $30.00.

A very powerful crank-operated repeat-ing air rifle was made by Charles Bunge at Geneva, N. Y. It utilized the barrel and cylinder design of the 1851 Colt revolver, and the cylinder was loaded from the front end with .28 caliber lead balls.

Probably the firm of Oscar Will, founded in 1844 in Germany, is the oldest maker of crank air guns. This plant is now in East Germany under the Russians, but is still exporting guns to other parts of the world.

Guns similar to the Will guns were produced in America after the middle of the nineteenth century by a few makers. John Zuendorff, a New York City maker, produced crank-type guns that were used in the Civil War draft riots in New York City.

While operating in essentially the same way, there are several variations in the manner of cocking the spring-piston mechanism of these guns. Some used their trigger guard or an integral lever crank for cocking; others employed a detachable crank.

The pistol shown here was made by Al. Junk in Teplitz, Czechoslovakia. It is a shooting gallery type with a set trigger, and the barrel is shown tipped up for loading. The crank below the pistol is used for cocking the piston which operates in the cylinder next to the barrel. The crank is inserted in the opening directly above the trigger.

5 SPRING

In a spring-operated air gun, the air is compressed the moment the arm is fired, as compared to a pneumatic type in which the air is first compressed into a reservoir where it is retained until the gun is discharged. The spring-operated guns to be discussed in this category differ from the crank-operated type only in the manner of cocking. Instead of using a crank, they are cocked by pushing the barrel in or out, or tipping it down.

The most important name in the development of toy B-B guns and air rifles for target shooting and hunting small game is H. M. Quackenbush of Herkimer, N. Y. He first worked for Remington Arms, and in 1872 started his own business on a small scale. His first product was an air pistol patented in 1871, which was cocked by pushing in the barrel. Later, his number one air gun, which was cocked in the same manner, proved to be an effective substitute for the expensive crank-type spring gallery gun that had been produced in the 1860's. The crank gallery guns sold for around $35, whereas Quackenbush's gun sold for only $10. He also patented a method of manufacturing superior darts and slugs so that they fitted most of the air guns of that period, regardless of the variations in the barrel dimensions.

Two other men from the same area, Ben-jamin Haviland and G. P. Gunn, invented a very powerful air gun which was capable of firing both darts and .22 caliber rim-fire powder cartridges. This was made possible by "breaking" the gun at the hinged barrel and using a firing-pin insert, which was carried in the butt, to detonate the cartridge. These guns were first made and marketed by Haviland and Gunn in 1871, but they later sold their patents to Quackenbush, who began manufacturing them under his own name in 1876. Quackenbush was a merchandising genius, and licensed the manufacture of the guns in Germany. The German air gun industry of the twentieth century can all be traced directly to the production methods and licenses passed on to their firms by Quackenbush.

The pistol at the top was patented by Augustus Bedford and George Walker in 1876. This piece is cocked by pushing in the plunger located beneath the barrel, and a bolt-action device is employed for loading. The metal rod shown can be attached to either pistol to serve as a shoulder stock.

The pistol at the bottom was patented in 1871 by Pope in Boston. Pistols of this type were later manufactured by Quackenbush. The barrel is pulled out for cocking and loading, and they were recommended for military training use by General Sherman after the Civil War.

6 FIRST GAS (CO₂)

THE FATHER of the carbon dioxide gun, which is just now achieving real popularity for short-range target shooting, was Paul Giffard (1837-1897), a French engineer and inventor. Giffard is credited with over 200 patents for inventions, some of which are pneumatic tubes for mail delivery, the refrigerator, engines for compressing and liquefying gas, and the pneumatic telegraph.

In the field of air guns, his first patent was issued in England in 1862, and in the United States in 1864. This patent was for a single-shot pneumatic air gun with an improved form of pressure release. In 1872 he patented a gas cartridge and a rifle in which it was used. Although these 8 millimeter CO_2 cartridges were powerful, they could not compare with the power of powder cartridges, and this idea was not developed to any appreciable degree.

In 1889, he patented the system of rifles and pistols using carbonic acid gas (CO_2) as a propellant, and persuaded France's most famous arms maker, Manufacture d'Armes et Cycles de St. Etienne, at Loire, to manufacture these arms. From advertisements in French periodicals of the day, it is evident that Giffard and many French military experts expected the new CO_2, guns to revolutionize warfare. It is hard to imagine how a man of Giffard's scientific standing and achievement could have so over-rated the value of his gas weapons, since they never were a match for powder cartridge firearms. The first Giffard CO_2 rifles and pistols were very well made, but cost more to make than comparable powder arms. However, they were cheaper to operate because of the low cost of propellant and bullets. The CO_2 cylinders used on the guns were sold on an exchange basis.

He later developed an improved hammerless model of this same rifle, which was produced by the Giffard Gun Co. formed in London. The impossibility of keeping the valve airtight, combined with the difficulty of obtaining refills of the CO_2 cylinders prevented these weapons from becoming very popular, and they were only produced for a few years.

Obviously, the greatest advantage of a CO_2 arm over other air guns is the lack of labor required on the part of the shooter to fire the weapon. About this same time, however, German arms makers were far along on the manufacture of an inexpensive spring air rifle requiring only one movement of the barrel to prepare it for firing.

The Giffard pistol above was the first ever made to use CO_2 as a propellant. The CO_2 is stored in the cylinder below the barrel, and the power can be adjusted by a screw which regulates the fall of the hammer.

7 MODERN

ToDAY'S MODERN AIR GUNS are manufactured in three basic types, just as were their forerunners centuries before. These types are the pneumatic, spring, and gas (CO₂). Pistols illustrating each of these categories are shown above.

The top pneumatic or compressed air pistol is a .22 caliber single-shot model 132 as manufactured by the Benjamin Air Rifle Co., St. Louis, Missouri. This piece is pumped up before each shot by pulling the wooden handle, located underneath the barrel, down and forward. Five to twelve strokes are usually required, depending on the power desired. All current pneumatic air arms are of American manufacture.

The .22 caliber spring-type pistol in the center is manufactured by Webley and Scott of Birmingham, England. This gun is precision made, and considered by many to be the aristocrat of air pistols. The barrel, which acts as a cocking lever, is pulled upward to cock the piston in the cylinder.

The pistol at the bottom is a Model 600 gas (CO₂) pistol manufactured by Crosman Arms Co., Fairport, New York. It is a .22 caliber semi-automatic with magazine capacity for ten shots. The disposable "powerlet" shown below the pistol contains enough carbon dioxide for up to forty shots. Practically all of today's gas-operated weapons are manufactured in the United States.

The pneumatic pistol has a muzzle velocity of 380 feet per second, while the other two have velocities of 340 feet per second.

"Flintlock" pneumatic air gun made by Thomas Bate in London about 1780. Compressed air is stored in the spherical steel reservoir. The flintlock serves only to activate the valve mechanism which supplies air to discharge the bullet. There are several schools of thought concerning the use of a flintlock on air weapons. Some argue that, since air guns were outlawed in various countries, the lock served to disguise them. Others feel that these guns were simply styled to resemble contemporary flintlocks of the period in much the same way that modern air pistols are made to look like automatics.

Engraved crank-spring air gun made in New York City by Joseph Lurch about 1865. Guns of this type were used in shooting galleries shortly before and after the Civil War. The makers were usually of German extraction. American gallery guns were the spring-piston type with leather bushings. They had smooth bores which were designed to shoot darts. By inserting a detachable crank into the opening above the trigger, the piston is drawn back under spring tension. When the trigger is pulled, the piston is driven forward in the cylinder to provide compressed air for bullet propulsion. These guns were breechloaders, and the specimen shown here twists one-quarter turn to the right for loading.

Pneumatic air gun with butt reservoir, made by Conway of Manchester, England around 1820. This is a back action air gun, since the striker is cocked by being pushed forward rather than to the rear as was generally the case. The inventor of this system is unknown, as is the purpose behind its design.

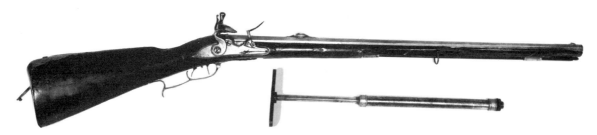

Flintlock air rifle, complete with pump, made by Wentzlav in Ehrenbreitstein, Germany around 1725. Occasionally, this type has been erroneously referred to as a combined flint and air gun. The flint mechanism serves only to operate the valve that permits a portion of the compressed air stored in the butt reservoir to escape to fire the bullet. Inasmuch as there is no vent at the barrel breech, the gun cannot be operated as a firearm. The pump is attached to the reservoir through a covered opening in the butt plate.

Single shot pneumatic six-millimeter air gun patented in 1862 by Paul Giffard, and made in St. Etienne, France. The tubular air reservoir below the barrel is pumped up with the pump shown below the gun. When the trigger is pressed, a plunger opens the valve to release the entire compressed air charge in the cylinder. These guns are very powerful and fire a report comparable to that made by a weapon using gunpowder. The gun shown here is breech-loading, and is equipped with a breech-tap to accommodate round lead bullets.

Cased English pneumatic air gun and rifle combination made by Thomas Bate in London, circa 1780. Accessories include bullet mold, air pump and wrench, spherical bronze reservoirs, and both a smoothbore and rifled barrel. The pump is used to charge the reservoirs to a pressure of about 500 to 700 lbs. per square inch. Usually about one stroke of the pump is required for each pound of pressure. A filled reservoir contains enough air for 20 to 25 shots; however, the power gets progressively weaker with each discharge.

English walking stick air rifle equipped with a breech tap for loading, complete with pump and cocking key in its original mahogany case. Although cane guns were also made as percussion and cartridge weapons, they achieved their greatest effectiveness as air canes. Almost all of these were made in England during the nineteenth century. Most of them had straight stocks and, since there was very little recoil, they could be rested against the cheek for firing. Bent or crank-shaped ones were shot from the shoulder. All air canes unscrewed into two sections, one containing the air reservoir, and the other the barrel and air release mechanism. They were extremely powerful, with a killing range of over 100 feet.

Giffard gas (CO₂) rifle made by the Giffard Gun Co., Ltd., London. Paul Giffard was the inventor of gas-operated arms, which he patented in 1889. His first gas rifles were manufactured in St. Etienne, France, and had an exposed hammer. Several years later, he formed the London company, which manufactured a hammerless model. Enough carbon dioxide is stored in the reservoir below the barrel to fire 120 to 800 shots, depending upon the caliber of the barrel. The guns were made in 4½ millimeter, 6 millimeter, and 8 millimeter calibers, and there was an adjustment to regulate power. A counting device was also provided to register the number of shots fired. Gas refill cylinders were sold on an exchange basis.

South American blowguns. The blowgun at the top is from Peru and is constructed of a split tube, which is held together by tree bark wrapped the full length of the gun. The one below was made by the Jivaro Indians of Ecuador, and is entirely coated with a native substance. The small cup affixed to the gun just forward of the bone mouthpiece is used to carry the poisonous curare in which the darts are dipped. The quiver shown between the guns contains a supply of darts. The gourd is filled with tree cotton, which is wrapped around one end of the dart to form a seal in the blowgun. This seal is necessary in order for the dart to be blown from the gun.

German 18th century bar-lock pneumatic air rifle with wooden trigger guard and patch box in stock. Compressed air is pumped into the spherical bronze reservoir. This rifle also has an auxiliary hair trigger for greater accuracy. Two forms of bar-lock air guns were made. One form has the ball centrally located below the stock and forward of the trigger guard, and the valve stud protrudes through the barrel. In the other type, the ball is to the right below the lock plate with the valve stud protruding through an opening in the lock plate. The bar-lock action is a direct striking device which releases the necessary amount of air from the reservoir and then slips past the valve to permit its closing.

Austrian bellows-type air gun made by Maringer in Vienna around 1700. The German name for these guns is Bolzenbuchse, which means "dart gun." The buttstock is hollowed out, and contains a bellows. By cranking the square male stud protruding from the butt, the bellows are forced open by means of a spring. When the trigger is pulled, the air that is compressed by the sudden closing of the bellows forces the bullet from the barrel. Bolzenbuchse guns were made mostly by German and Austrian gunsmiths for indoor target shooting. They were very ornate and costly, and it was common practice for shooting clubs to purchase one for the use of its members.

Pneumatic air gun with the reservoir surrounding the barrel, made by Jover in London around 1775. In this type of weapon, the pump is located in the butt. Barrel-jacketed guns were produced in both Germany and England, but never in any great quantity, and specimens today are very scarce. They later were replaced by butt and spherical reservoir-type pneumatic guns, since this type utilized only one valve, whereas two were necessary in the former.

Pneumatic air gun made by Scarlett in Sheffield, England circa 1825, with spherical air reservoir located below the barrel. Pneumatic air guns emigrated from the Continent to England, and since in the latter part of the eighteenth century England was producing the finest firearms in the world, English gunsmiths developed these guns to an even greater degree in both beauty and performance. The spherical reservoirs were made in copper, brass, and steel.

Unusual ratchet-cocking air pistol operated by lever. The small caliber barrel located above the air cylinder is loaded by swinging the breech plug to one side. Parker and Hale, a large mail order house for guns in England, prepared a patent application for this pistol, but the patent was never issued. In view of this, it is possible that this pistol is the patent model.

Pneumatic butt-reservoir air gun. This type of gun with the lock mechanism built on the outside of the lock plate was made between 1700 and 1750 in the northern part of Germany. It is impossible to explain the reason for this construction. Two possibilities are that the exposed mechanism was made so that the gun would not have to be dismantled for repairs or so the air could pass directly from the stock to the barrel with a minimum of obstruction

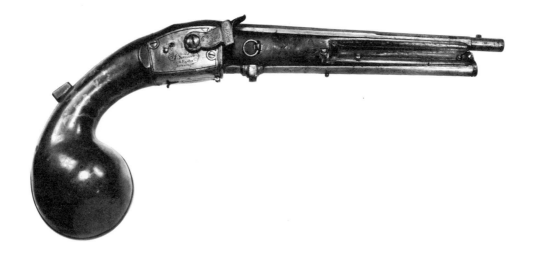

Pneumatic air pistol made by Jean and Nicholas Bouillet in Paris about 1730. Compressed air is stored in the bulbous stock, and the bullet magazine is located below the barrel. This pistol is made up of 107 parts. After the stock is un- screwed, a hand pump is used to charge it with compressed air. By partially revolving the barrel section, the hammer is cocked, a bullet is fed to the breech, and a concealed trigger drops into firing position.

Haviland and Gunn combination air and .22 caliber rim-fire cartridge gun, patented in Ilion, New York in 1871. When the trigger guard is pushed forward, the breech end of the barrel "breaks," and thereby cocks the piston under spring ten- sion in the cylinder. To fire a .22 powder cartridge, a firing pin, carried in a recess in the underside of the butt plate, is inserted in the air vent of the cylinder. When the trigger is pulled, the compressed air forces this firing pin against the cartridge head to detonate the cartridge.

PART III

Cartridges and Primers

The cartridge specimens selected for this section have been divided into nine categories, beginning with the first paper forms and continuing through the modern rimless types. All cartridges are pictured in actual size.

Pictured after the cartridges are the several means of supplying the necessary flame or spark to ignite black gunpowder. Following this are the various primers, pictured in actual size, which supplied chemical ignition, first to the gunpowder in the barrel, and later to the propellant charge placed in the cartridge case.

DEVELOPMENT OF THE
CARTRIDGE

PAPER	
COMBUSTIBLE	
SEPARATE-PRIMED	
SELF-CONTAINED	
PATENT IGNITION	
RIM-FIRE	
CENTER-FIRE (EARLY)	
CENTER-FIRE (INSIDE PRIMED)	
CENTER-FIRE (MODERN)	

DEVELOPMENT OF THE CARTRIDGE

With the use of gunpowder in hand fire-arms about the middle of the fourteenth century, it became inevitable that many advances would be made in its manner of use in detonating firearms. At first, gunpowder was carried in powder horns or containers, and the projectiles were carried separately. It is most likely that paper cartridges came into use about 1550, during the matchlock period. At first, the powder was simply measured into paper packets. Toward the latter part of the sixteenth century, references were made to both powder and ball being combined in the same paper wrapping. This first type of cartridge was used by both sportsmen and the military.

During this same period, "bandoliers" came into use. The "bandolier" was a belt, usually worn diagonally across the chest. Suspended from the belt by means of a cord were about one dozen wooden or metal containers holding pre-measured amounts of gunpowder. The shooter also carried a bag of bullets and a flask of powder for priming purposes. For obvious reasons, the "bandolier" was not too practical, since the containers rattled against one another, and the cords often became tangled. However, the greatest drawback was the possibility of the containers catching fire and exploding in the shooter's face, due to their proximity to the priming flash.

Paper containers for cartridges continued to be in use through the American Civil War before they gave way completely to metallic cartridges. The term "cartridge," as previously used, applied only to the powder and ball combined in a paper wrapper. The modern definition of a cartridge is, briefly, fixed ammunition having gunpowder, projectile, and primer combined in a cardboard or metal case as a self-contained single unit. The first self-contained cartridge having the propellant, primer and projectile combined in a single unit was patented in France on September 29, 1812, by a Swiss artillery officer, Jean Samuel Pauly, who was working in Paris.

A Pauly pistol for firing these early cartridges is shown in the first section on firearms. The first Pauly cartridges consisted of a brass base, called a rosette, to which was attached a paper case. The rosette had a 1/8" diameter cavity in its center, which contained the primer. This primer consisted of a mixture of potassium chlorate, sulphur, and charcoal, with a small amount of gum arabic added. After a pinch of a priming mixture was placed in the cavity, this powder was covered with a small piece of paper to prevent the powder from spilling out and becoming damp. His first paper cartridge was difficult to make, and shortly afterwards he replaced the paper case with one made of brass, making this case an integral part of the rosette. An example of this all-brass cartridge is shown in Figure 1. Figure 2 shows a cased set of Pauly cartridge-making tools which were used to make the world's first self-contained cartridge, in which the bullet, propellant, and primer were contained in one unit.

These tools have been removed from the case in Figure 3. At the lower left is an ebony-handled, 3-bladed screwdriver. Adjacent to this is a spring-loaded steel punch, which is used to cut out cardboard, felt, or leather circular discs that are used in the construction of the cartridge. These discs have a hole in the center to accommodate the threaded screw of the rosette. Alongside the punch, this circular cutout is shown fastened to one of the rosettes. The apparent use of the clamp would seem to be that of securing the paper to the mandrel while the glue is drying, to form the cylindrical paper cartridge case. One end of the paper cylinder is covered with thin paper so as to completely seal that end, after which the case is filled with the powder and the round lead bullet. The tip of the cartridge is tied, as can be seen in the photograph, to prevent the bullet from falling out of the case. The ebony-handled tool at the top right is used to extract the Pauly rosette from the barrel. As illustrated, the tip of the extractor is shown engaging the circular groove on the face of the rosette. The brass object below the extractor contains oil or a suitable cleaning solution, and the pick which screws into the top is shown piercing the vent-opening of the rosette. Below this is a brass powder measure. The rosette to the right of the lead bullet clearly shows the opening, referred to

as a "bassinet" by Pauly, in which the priming compound was placed.

The Pauly brass cartridge was the first center-fire cartridge to be used. About the only drawback to this cartridge was the fact that the brass case was too thick to permit its expansion to make a gas-tight seal in the barrel. Insofar as self-contained cartridges were concerned, nothing further was developed until about 1829, when Johann Nikolaus von Dreyse invented a self-contained needle cartridge.

The cartridge specimens shown on the following pages are grouped together in nine categories, as can be seen on the chart showing the chronology of their development.

Before going into the various cartridge categories, it might be well to briefly outline the several methods by which cartridges are classified. As will soon become evident, there is no rhyme or reason to the "system" used to classify cartridges.

In America, cartridges are classified as rim-fires, center-fire metallics, and shot shells. During the period when black powder was in use, cartridges were often named from their bore diameter, followed by the amount in grains of black powder packed in the case, and often by the weight of the bullet in grains. For example, the 44-40-200 is .44 caliber, having 40 grains of black powder propelling a 200 grain lead bullet. Caliber size is expressed in hundredths of an inch, that is, .50 caliber is one-half inch. In the European metric system, 25.4 millimeters equals one inch. A few smokeless

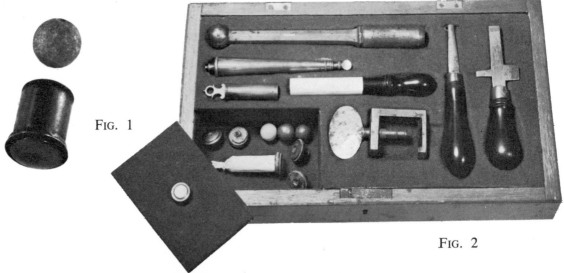

Fig. 1

Fig. 2

powder cartridges are also named in this manner, such as the 30-30 and the 30-40. A lot of cartridges are named from the bore diameter, followed by the name of the company manufacturing them. An example of this is the 44-40, which Winchester prefers to call the .44 W. C. F., meaning .44 caliber Winchester center-fire. Sometimes the name of the weapon for which the cartridge is intended is used, such as the .401 Winchester S. L. (self-loading), or the .45 A. C. P. (automatic Colt pistol).

Shotgun gauges are based on the number of balls of the bore diameter necessary to weigh one pound. For instance, 12 balls of the diameter of a 12-gauge bore weigh one pound. In the smaller bore 16-gauge shotgun, it takes 16 balls to weigh one pound. Currently, 10-, 12-, 16-, 18-, 20-, and 28-gauge guns are made in the United States, 12-gauge being the most popular. The .410 shotgun, although commonly referred to as 410-gauge, is actually not a gauge, but a caliber.

Rifled barrels have a series of lands and grooves, the lands being the high point and the grooves the low point of the rifling. The caliber or bore of a rifled barrel is the diameter measured from land to land. Some cartridges, however, are named from the groove diameter of the barrel.

In the popular 30-06 American cartridge, the 30 refers to the caliber, and the 06 means that it was adopted in 1906. Recently, descriptive names have been combined with the caliber, such as the .22 Hornet, .220 Swift, and .22 Varminter. In many instances, the caliber designator of a cartridge is not the actual caliber at all, being either slightly larger or smaller than the bore diameter of the gun in which they are fired.

European cartridges are frequently named from the bore diameter in millimeters, followed by the case length, also in millimeters. When the United States manufactures a British or German cartridge, or vice versa, the cartridge designator is changed. For example, the American 30-06 cartridge, when manufactured in Germany, is called the 7.62 x 63.

As for bullet classification, a cartridge with a paper patch bullet means that paper is wrapped around the bullet at the point where the bullet joins the case. A swaged bullet is one which is formed to its size under pressure. Some bullets are referred to as boat-tail type, which means that they are slightly tapered at the base. Bullets have been shaped to almost every style imaginable, including triangular and square shapes. They have also been metal-jacketed, metal-tipped, hollow-pointed, just to name a few variations.

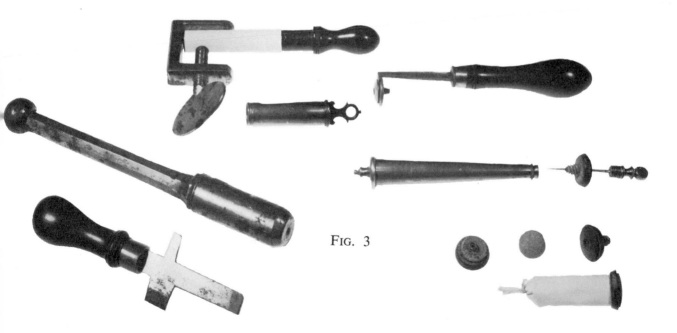

FIG. 3

PAPER

The first cartridges to be used were merely a measured amount of gunpowder wrapped in paper and tied with a string. Later, the bullet was combined with the powder in the paper case. As previously stated, these first cartridges appeared around the middle of the sixteenth century and continued to be in use through the American Civil War. Generally speaking, the method of manufacturing a paper cartridge consists of wrapping a piece of paper around a stick, the diameter of which corresponds with the bore of the gun. The paper is then pulled back from the stick so that the end can be pinched together and tied. The stick is then removed so that a lead ball can be inserted in the tube. The stick is then reinserted to hold the shape of the paper tube while a string is tied to hold the ball in place. Now the stick is removed, and a measured amount of powder is poured into the case. The end of the case is pinched and folded, forming a tail, to seal the cartridge.

Military instructions covering the use of paper cartridges specified that the soldier was to tear open the cartridge, pour the powder into the barrel, followed by the bullet with the paper wrapper removed. The wrapper was then rammed down to serve as a wad. Usually a small amount of the powder was used to fill the priming pan. No doubt everyone is familiar with the illustrations of American soldiers in both the Revolutionary and Civil Wars biting off the tail end of a paper cartridge, preparatory to loading his gun.

The first paper cartridges had round balls for projectiles. Round balls could be readily loaded into smoothbore muskets. However, with the introduction of rifled barrels, it became obvious that another type of bullet was needed to increase the speed of loading. Various shapes were experimented with, and finally a cylindro-conoidal shape with a hollow base proved to be the solution to the problem. This type of bullet could be practically dropped down the barrel when loading, and the hollow base was expanded by the explosion of the charge to engage the rifling in the barrel. In England, Norton and Greener pioneered in the development of this type of bullet, and their work was followed in France by Captain C. E. Minié. The base of Minié's bullet contained an iron cup which was driven forward by force of the explosion to expand the hollow base. An American, James H. Burton of Harper's Ferry Armory, redesigned the cavity somewhat so that no wedge or cup was required, making the bullet self-expanding. This bullet was adopted by the United States in 1855, and is commonly known as the Minié ball. With this development, the smoothbore musket was finished as a military arm.

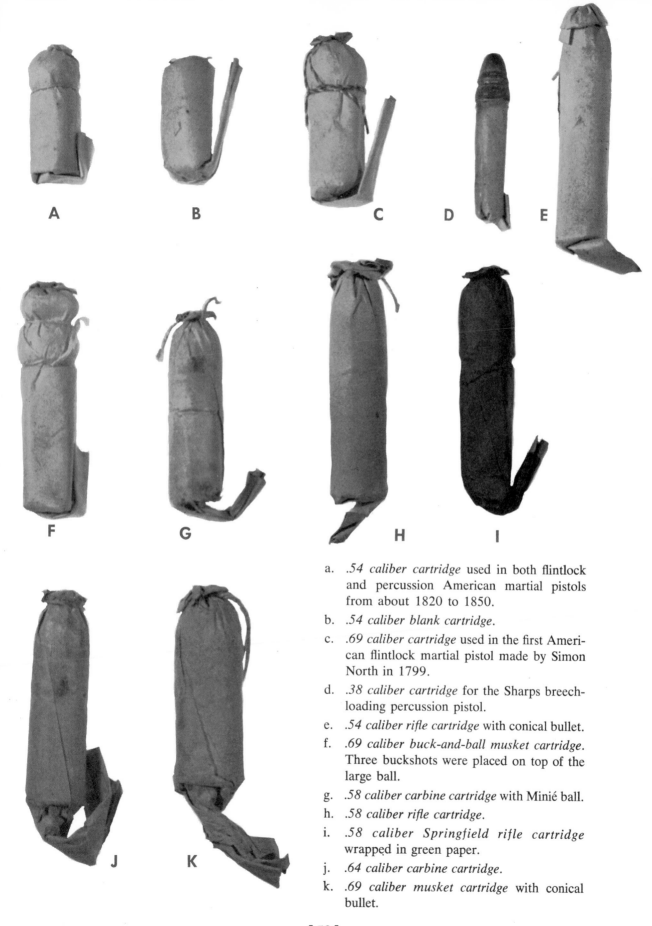

A   B   C   D   E

F   G   H   I

J   K

a. *.54 caliber cartridge* used in both flintlock and percussion American martial pistols from about 1820 to 1850.

b. *.54 caliber blank cartridge.*

c. *.69 caliber cartridge* used in the first American flintlock martial pistol made by Simon North in 1799.

d. *.38 caliber cartridge* for the Sharps breech-loading percussion pistol.

e. *.54 caliber rifle cartridge* with conical bullet.

f. *.69 caliber buck-and-ball musket cartridge.* Three buckshots were placed on top of the large ball.

g. *.58 caliber carbine cartridge* with Minié ball.

h. *.58 caliber rifle cartridge.*

i. *.58 caliber Springfield rifle cartridge* wrapped in green paper.

j. *.64 caliber carbine cartridge.*

k. *.69 caliber musket cartridge* with conical bullet.

COMBUSTIBLE · Paper, Skin, Collodion, Linen and Foil

Combustible-envelope cartridges appeared towards the latter part of the second quarter of the nineteenth century. The cases that held the powder charge of these cartridges were made of such materials as paper, skin, collodion, linen, foil, etc. All of these were heavily treated with nitrate, which made them easily inflammable, so that they were completely consumed when the cartridges were ignited. History does not tell us who was the first to produce this type of cartridge, but they were produced by a number of firms in the 1850's.

Combustible cartridges were packed in a number of different ways to protect them from damage, as they were very fragile. Most of them were placed in a wooden block which was bored out to accommodate five or six cartridges, depending on the number of cartridges needed to fill a revolver cylin-

der. Others were merely wrapped in paper or came packed in cardboard cartons. The cartridges for single-shot carbines and rifles came in boxes containing 7 to 50 rounds. The English combustible cartridges were almost always wrapped in a protective paper wrapper which was readily removed by pulling a tear tab or ribbon.

The chief feature of combustible cartridges was their convenience. The most common type of skin cartridges were made by D. C. Sage & Co. under two Hotchkiss patents. The first type, known as "waterproof" skin cartridges, was made with two strips of membrane wrapped around the powder in a spiral manner. The other type was the "seamless" skin cartridge, with a one-piece membrane covering. The covering for skin cartridges consisted of the outer membrane of pig or cattle intestines.

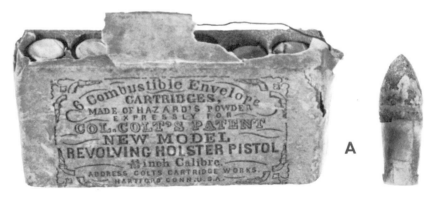

A

a. Open package showing six *.44 caliber combustible-envelope cartridges.* A waterproof paper covering is wrapped around a wooden block, which has been drilled to hold six of these cartridges, that being enough to fill this particular revolver cylinder. The cartridge shown alongside has been removed from the package. The fragility of these cartridges necessitated packing them in this manner.

[60]

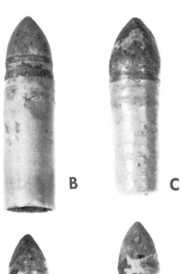

b. *.52 caliber linen cartridge* for Sharps carbine. This cartridge has a linen case with its base end covered with very thin paper, so that it could be readily ignited by the flame penetrating the nipple. It was used in the Sharps sporting and military arms both before and during the Civil War.

c. *Johnson and Dow .58 caliber skin cartridge* for rifles.

d. *.44 caliber combustible cartridge,* black collodion-coated, to make the case waterproof. This cartridge was made by the Hazard Powder Co., Hazardville, Connecticut. It was patented March 18, 1862 for use in the Colt percussion Army pistol. This waterproof cartridge was patented by B. L. Budd and R. O. Doremus.

e. *.44 caliber combustible paper envelope cartridge* for the Colt percussion revolver. These cartridges saw much service in the early frontier days and during the Civil War.

f. *.36 caliber skin cartridge* made of animal tissue, designed expressly for Colt cap-and-ball revolvers.

g. *British .36 caliber foil cartridge* made by Eley Bros. in London for use in the Colt percussion revolver. For protection, the cartridge has a paper wrapper which can be easily removed by pulling the tear tab.

h. *British .44 caliber combustible paper cartridge* made by Eley Bros. for use in the .44 caliber Colt percussion revolver.

i. *Paper-covered shot cartridge* designed for use in muzzle-loading shotguns. This cartridge was also made by Eley Bros.

SEPARATE-PRIMED · Paper, Cloth, Rubber, Metallic

Separate-primed cartridges have cartridge cases of various materials, and contain only a bullet and powder for propulsion. The ignition of these cartridges depended on the fire generated from a percussion cap, disc primer, or tape primer. The bases of the separate-primed cartridges had small flash holes to receive the flame.

A

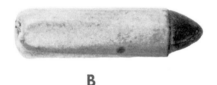

B

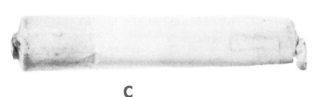

C

a. On August 10, 1848, Walter Hunt secured a patent for ". . . . a ball for firearms, with a cavity to contain the charge of powder for propelling said ball, in which cavity and powder is secured by means of a cap enclosing the back end." The base of this "rocket ball" was enclosed with a cork disc which had a hole in the center to receive the flash from a Maynard tape primer. Twenty of these were carried in a tubular magazine below the barrel of a Jennings rifle. This cartridge is .54 caliber and is stamped on the side "Patent 1848."

b. *.50 caliber Gallager brass-and-paper cartridge.* These cartridges were used in a percussion carbine patented by Gallager in 1860. Over eight million of these cartridges were purchased by the United States Army during the Civil War.

c. *.577 Enfield cartridge* used in the British muzzle-loading Enfield rifle, and also in the American Civil War Greene breech-loading rifle. To load, a bullet was seated in the chamber of the gun before inserting the paper cartridge. After acting as a gas seal for the firing of the forward bullet, the bullet contained in the paper cartridge was then pushed forward by the bolt and discharged by the powder charge of the next cartridge. These cartridges were partly responsible for setting off the 1857 rebellion in India, since it was rumored that they were greased with the fat of pigs and cows. Moslems and Hin-

D

E

F

G

H

I

dus refused to touch the cartridges, as they had to be bitten before inserting them into the muzzle, and their religion forbade them to eat either of these animals.

d. *.50 caliber Smith cartridge* with case made of brass foil and paper. This was one of several types of cartridges used in the Smith carbine.

e. *.50 caliber Smith cartridge* with rubber case used in the Smith breech-loading percussion rifled carbine. In 1857, Gilbert Smith patented this cartridge with the idea of having the rubber case expand during the firing to form a seal in the barrel.

f. *.50 caliber Maynard brass cartridge* used in both sporting and military breech-loading carbines.

g. *.50 caliber Gallager cartridge* with all brass case. Very few of these cartridges were made as compared to the Gallager brass-and-paper cartridges.

h. *.54 caliber Burnside cartridge* with brass tapered case. This cartridge was patented March 25, 1856 by Ambrose Burnside, who later became a general in the Union Army during the Civil War. They were used in the Burnside breech-loading carbine, and were ignited by the fire from a percussion cap. Almost 22 million were purchased during the Civil War.

i. *.56 caliber Billinghurst Requa cartridge* with brass case. This cartridge was used in a Civil War volley gun which had 24 barrels in a single row. Twenty-four of these cartridges were loaded at one time by means of a special device. In firing, a train of priming powder was poured, extending the entire length of the breechblock. The spark from a percussion cap ignited the first cartridge, and the rest were set off in rapid succession.

SELF-CONTAINED · Paper, Metallic

Following the Pauly self-contained, paper-and-brass cartridges discussed at the beginning of this section, needle-fire cartridges with the powder, bullet and primer all placed in one unit were the first self-contained cartridges to be in general use. Johann Nikolaus von Dreyse, the inventor of the needle gun, worked as an apprentice under Pauly in Paris from 1808 to 1814. When Pauly went to England, Dreyse returned to Prussia, where he invented the muzzle-loading needle gun some time between 1827 and 1829. His first needle gun was loaded with loose powder poured down the barrel, followed by a ball containing a cavity for fulminate. The cavity was sealed with thin paper. A few years later, loose powder was dispensed with in needle guns, and was packed together with the fulminate and bullet in a paper or cardboard cartridge.

An Englishman by the name of Abraham A. Moser patented a needle-fire cartridge in England in 1831. Moser's patent was not for a self-contained cartridge, but instead called for ignition of gunpowder that was poured down the barrel by a needle striking fulminate located at the base of the bullet. At the time the patent was granted, Moser was in communication with a man on the continent who probably was Dreyse. Moser's needle cartridge differed from Dreyse's only in the manner in which the ball traveled down the barrel.

In the German needle-fire cartridges, the priming was placed in a recess in the cardboard sabot located at the base of the bullet. In order to detonate the primer, it was necessary for a long needle to penetrate the cartridge base and travel completely through the powder charge. During the powder explosion, the needle was exposed to intense heat, and therefore soon became brittle and had to be replaced frequently. French and English needle cartridges overcame this drawback by placing the primer just inside the cartridge head. The Germans placed the primer ahead of the powder charge because they felt that more velocity was gained by having the charge burn backward. No other countries used this type of front ignition, and the Germans themselves discontinued its use after the Franco-Prussian War. Tests conducted about ten years ago at the Frankford Arsenal verified the fact that bullet velocity was increased by about seven per cent with front ignition.

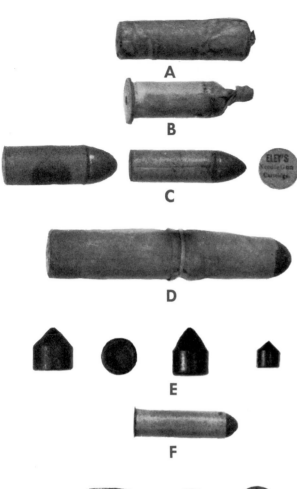

a. *German paper-covered needle cartridge* used in a sporting rifle.

b. *German rim type 9.95mm needle-fire ball cartridge,* used in a light rifle.

c. *110 bore and 90 bore needle gun cartridges* made by Eley Bros. of London. These cartridges have the fulminate located in the head rather than next to the bullet, as in the German needle cartridges.

d. *11mm French needle-fire cartridge* used in the Chassepot breech-loading military rifle. This cartridge was used by the French in the Franco-Prussian War of 1870, and the fulminate is located in the cartridge head.

e. *A group of several sizes of Gaupillat cartridges,* patented in 1854. These cartridges were placed in a tubular magazine above the barrel, and were dropped down into firing position by gravity. They are quite similar to the American Volcanic cartridges, since primer and powder are contained within the bullet.

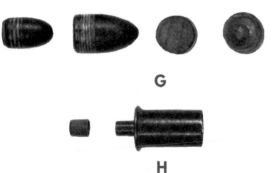

f. *7mm cartridge* for use in a cane gun.

g. *.31 and .41 caliber Volcanic cartridges,* patented in 1856, although Volcanic arms were patented in 1854. The base view at the left illustrates the type with cork-covered base, and the one at the right is covered with a metal washer. Volcanic cartridges were the first American cartridges to have primer, propellant powder, and bullet all in one unit.

h. *.41 caliber auxiliary reloadable* insert containing powder and ball, and fitted with a percussion cap. This insert was used in the Williamson derringer.

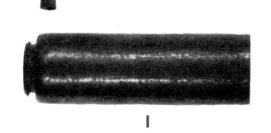

i. *16-gauge reloadable steel shell,* patented in 1866 and used in the Roper four-shot revolving shotgun. This shell has a recess in its center to receive a percussion cap.

PATENT IGNITION

Included in this category are the following types: pin-fire, teat-fire, cup-primer, lip-fire, annular-rim, and inside pin-fire, all of which have brass or copper cases.

The pin-fire is the oldest of this group, and was used in considerable numbers by both Union and Confederate forces during the Civil War. Pin-fire weapons enjoyed far greater popularity in Europe than in this country, and even today they remain in use in other parts of the world. These cartridges have a pin which protrudes through the cartridge case near the head. The end of the pin inside the case rests in a percussion cap containing fulminate, and when the hammer drives the pin into this priming mixture, the cartridge is detonated. The first pin-fire cartridge was invented by M. Lefaucheux of Paris about 1836. His cartridge had a cardboard case and brass head. The cartridge was almost rimless, and was removed from the barrel by pulling on the pin.

In 1846, another French gunsmith, M. Houllier, patented a pin-fire cartridge which consisted of a full length case constructed of thin copper or brass. Now, for the first time, the thin metallic case could be expanded at the time of the explosion to form a gas-tight seal, and then return almost immediately to its original size for extraction from the chamber. For this feature alone, Houllier deserves a prominent place among those who contributed to cartridge development. With the proper tools, pin-fire cartridges can be easily reloaded.

The teat-fire and cup-primer cartridges were manufactured solely to evade infringement on the Smith & Wesson patent which called for loading the cylinder chamber from the breech end. A detailed account of these evasion pistols can be found in the last section of this book.

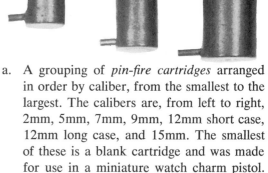

A

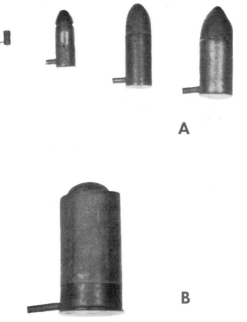

B

a. A grouping of *pin-fire cartridges* arranged in order by caliber, from the smallest to the largest. The calibers are, from left to right, 2mm, 5mm, 7mm, 9mm, 12mm short case, 12mm long case, and 15mm. The smallest of these is a blank cartridge and was made for use in a miniature watch charm pistol. The 12mm cartridges were used considerably in pin-fire revolvers by both Union and Confederate forces in the Civil War.

b. *20-gauge French shotgun cartridge* with copper base and cardboard case. This cartridge is quite similar in construction to the first Lefaucheux pin-fire cartridge.

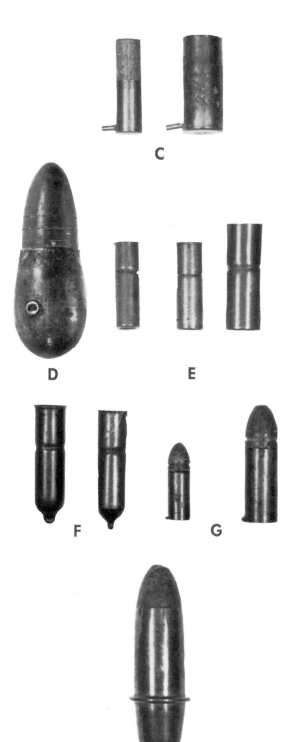

C

D   E

F   G

H

c. *7mm and 12mm pin-fire shot cartridges.*

d. *.58 caliber Gallager and Gladding inside pin-fire cartridge* with brass case, patented July 12, 1859. This is probably the rarest of all cartridges, and was used in the Schubarth rifle. In this cartridge, the pin is located inside the case with one end inserted in a percussion cap and the other confined in the blister on the side of the case. The breech of the Schubarth rifle has a cavity to accommodate this blister. When the blister is struck a blow, the pin is driven into the percussion cap in the same way as a conventional pin-fire cartridge. A Minié bullet is pressed into the mouth of the cartridge case and is sealed with tallow.

e. *.28, .30, and .42 caliber copper cup-primer cartridges.* These cartridges have a hollow base and were made for use in front-loading revolvers which were made for the express purpose of circumventing the Smith & Wesson patent calling for breechloading of cartridges in a revolver cylinder. These cartridges were patented July 12, 1859 by Willard C. Ellis and John C. White.

f. *.32 caliber teat-fire copper cartridges* made for use in teat-fire revolvers which were also made to circumvent the Smith & Wesson patent. As can be seen, the cartridge at the left has a flat teat, while the other has a round teat. This cartridge was patented *January 5, 1864 by D. Williamson,* and they were also made in .45 caliber.

g. *.25 and .36 caliber copper case lip-fire cartridges.* On September 25, 1860, E. Allen patented this cartridge, which was similar to a rim-fire cartridge, except that it had the fulminate placed in a small lip at the base of the cartridge. A .44 caliber cartridge of this type was also made.

h. *.50 caliber Crispin cartridge* patented August 8, 1865, and made for use in one model of the Smith breech-loading carbine. In this cartridge the fulminate is placed in the annular rim. Crispin cartridges were also made in .31 and .44 caliber.

[67]

RIM-FIRE

The rim-fire cartridge originated in France with the invention of the bulleted breech cap by Flobert about 1845. These first .22 caliber cartridges were used only for indoor target shooting, and the entire case was filled with fulminate powder which served both as primer and propellant. A round ball was inserted in the case, which resembled a musket cap of that period. In 1846, M. Houllier patented a one-piece copper case pin-fire and also a rim-fire cartridge, although no further work was done by him in developing the rim-fire idea.

Daniel B. Wesson was familiar with the Flobert B-B cap, and although he did not claim to be the inventor of the rim-fire cartridge, he did improve on this cartridge by lengthening the case to hold a black powder propellant charge, and an elongated conical-shaped bullet.

In 1857, Smith & Wesson produced their Model No. 1 revolver to use the No. 1 pistol cartridge, which was the first metallic cartridge to be produced in the United States. At first, the priming mixture was spread over the entire base. This practice caused the case to bulge upon firing and prevent the cylinder from rotating, and consequently the priming mixture was placed only in the cartridge rim.

These Smith & Wesson cartridges were very successful from the start. The Smith & Wesson cartridge known today as the .22 short was being produced at the rate of 30 million a year in 1870. Today, basically unchanged from its original form, more of these cartridges are manufactured than any other type in the world. After their first success, others immediately began to copy them. By the end of 1858, B. Tyler Henry was making the same type of cartridges in .44 caliber for use in his Henry rifle. Eventually, the rim-fire cartridge was increased to .58 caliber for use in military weapons.

Rim-fire cartridges had certain inherent drawbacks which eventually led to their replacement by center-fire cartridges. Chief among these was the fact that they were not generally considered reloadable. In this regard, it is interesting to note that in the 1870's some American Indians did reload rim-fire cartridges by drilling holes in the center of the cartridge heads and inserting musket caps. Also, there was the problem of distributing the fulminate priming compound evenly and continuously around the rim. Finally, there was the problem of making the cartridge rims strong enough to withstand the explosion of the larger caliber and at the same time soft enough to be dented by the fall of the hammer. This problem was more acute in the case of the larger caliber revolver cartridges than in rifles, since the latter had a breech bolt to back up against the cartridge head. Today the only rim-fire cartridges made are in .22 caliber.

All cartridges shown have copper cases.

a. *Original Smith & Wesson No. 1 pistol cartridge,* .22 caliber, with slightly indented head.

b. *4mm cartridge* used in the European target rifles.

c. *.22 caliber B-B or bullet breech cap.*

d. *.32 caliber short cartridge* with Merwin's patent case, having a conical depression in the base.

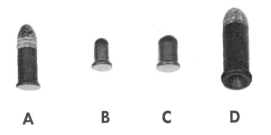

A   B   C   D

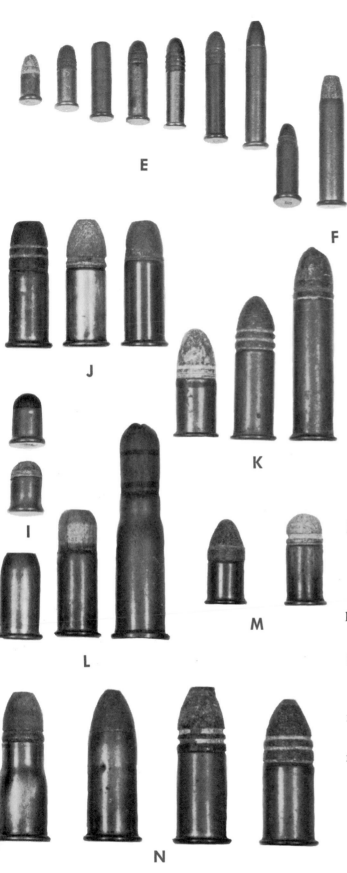

E

F

G

H

J

K

I

L

M

N

e. A grouping of *.22 caliber cartridges,* beginning with the C. B. cap, conical bullet cap, and showing various other members of the .22 family.

f. *.22 caliber Winchester automatic cartridge, .25 caliber Stevens cartridge,* and a shot cartridge.

g. *.32 caliber long and extra long cartridges.*

h. *.38 caliber short and long cartridges.*

i. *9mm gallery cap cartridges* used primarily for target shooting. The lower French cartridge is very similar in shape to the original Flobert B-B cap.

j. *.44 caliber Henry cartridges* showing the flat, pointed, and long case varieties. Henry cartridges made at the New Haven Arms Co. are stamped on the head with an H in honor of B. Tyler Henry.

k. *.44 caliber short, long and extra long cartridges.*

l. *.44 caliber blank cartridge,* .44 caliber shot cartridge, and .41 caliber Swiss shot cartridge.

m. *.41 caliber derringer and .41 caliber long cartridge.*

n. *Spencer cartridges,* used in the Spencer rifles and carbines. Originally patented in 1860. Left to right, they are the 56-46, the 56-50, the 56-52, and the 56-56. The 56-46 is a sporting cartridge, while the rest are military. The 56-52 has a .22 blank inserted in the tip of the bullet to make it an explosive cartridge.

[69]

When Pauly produced the world's first center-fire metallic cartridge about 1814, which was only seven years after Forsyth patented the percussion system of ignition, it is surprising that nothing further was done to develop the center-fire metallic cartridge until 1829 when a Frenchman named Pottet patented a metallic cartridge case which employed a percussion cap to furnish ignition.

The only appreciable drawback to the Pauly cartridge was the fact that the brass cartridge case was too thick to expand sufficiently during the explosion to make a gas-tight seal in the barrel breech.

One of the earliest modern metallic center-fire cartridges to be experimented with in the United States, was the Morse cartridge. A specimen of an early Morse cartridge is shown in Figure j. Morse received two patents in May and June of 1858. The first called for a pronged anvil against which a percussion cap was crushed. The second called for the cap, surrounded by a perforated rubber base, to be crushed on an anvil located in the cartridge base. Previously, in 1856, George Morse had invented a soft metal cartridge case which was designed to seal the breech of the breech-loading gun. The Morse cartridges were made at the Springfield Armory and later at the Frankford Arsenal.

Morse worked with the government in perfecting his center-fire cartridges, and in converting military muskets to use these cartridges, up to the beginning of the Civil War. Most of the equipment Morse was using was located at Harper's Ferry, and was captured by the South. Morse himself, being a Southerner, went South and contributed his efforts in making arms and ammunition for the Confederacy.

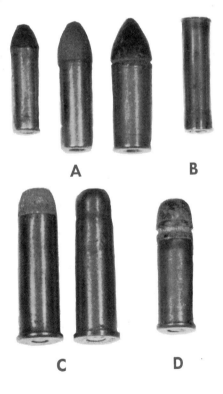

A   B

C   D

a. *.31, .36, and .44 caliber brass-case Thuer cartridges* used in the altered Colt percussion revolvers permitting the use of center-fire metallic cartridges. They were patented September 15, 1868 by F. A. Thuer, but were not very successful.

b. *.31 caliber front-loading center-fire cartridge* equipped with a Milbank primer. The gun which fired this cartridge is not known.

c. *44-40 brass-case center-fire cartridges* used in both the Model 1873 Winchester rifle and the Colt revolver. The cartridge at the right is called the game getter and is loaded with shot.

d. *.41 caliber brass-case cartridge* used in the Colt Model 1877 double-action Lightning revolver.

E   F   G

e. *.450 caliber British Boxer-type cartridge* with an iron base, for use in the .455 Adams revolver.

f. *.50 caliber brass-case cartridge* used in the Remington single-shot service pistol.

g. *.44, .45, and .455 caliber Colt cartridges.*

H   I   J

h. Left to right, the *.44 caliber S & W American, .44 caliber S & W Russian,* and the *.45 caliber S & W brass-case cartridges.*

i. *410-gauge shotgun shells,* one with all brass and one with cardboard case.

j. *.58 caliber Morse cartridge* with folded rim and a flat-type anvil fastened to the inside wall of the case. Morse cartridges were among the earliest of the center-fire cartridges.

K   L   M   N

k. *45-70-500 tin-case cartridge* with copper primer. This cartridge has a two-piece head and was made under the Morse patent of 1886 at the Frankford Arsenal.

l. *.40 caliber brass Maynard cartridge* with thick head.

m. *British .577 caliber Snider cartridge.* This was the first cartridge to be adopted by any government for use by its armed forces. The case is made of thin brass covered with brown paper and fastened to an iron base with a cup in the center. A percussion cap is used for a primer.

n. *.577-.450 British Boxer cartridge* used in the Martini-Henry rifle. The thin coiled .577 Snider brass case is necked down to a .45 caliber bullet. In April 1871, the Martini-Henry rifle and cartridge were adopted as the official arm and ammunition of the British armed forces, where it was used from 1871 to 1888.

CENTER-FIRE · Inside-Primed

Inside-primed cartridges fall into two basic categories. In the first, the fulminate is held in place inside the cartridge case by means of a cup or an anvil, which is fixed to the case by two crimps in the cartridge case itself. Except for the crimps, these cartridges look identical to rim-fire cartridges, since both have solid heads. The other type is Martin-primed, in which the one-piece head is folded around the primer, the primer being held secure by the pocket thus formed. These distinctions can be more easily understood by looking at the examples pictured.

Many experiments with early center-fire cartridges took place at the Frankford Arsenal in Philadelphia. During the period of the Civil War, nothing much was done toward experimenting with and developing the center-fire cartridge. When it became evident that the center-fire would replace the rim-fire, experimental work was begun immediately toward this end. During this period, the Ordnance Board decided in favor of a .50 caliber Model 1866 breechloader. The cartridge to be used was a .50 caliber center-fire with 70 grains of black powder and a 450 grain conical bullet, commonly called the 50-70.

The first inside-primed center-fire cartridges for the altered Springfield muskets were made between October 1866 and March 1868. These bar-anvil types were invented in June 1866 by E. H. Martin, who was employed at the National Armory in Springfield, Massachusetts, for cartridge development work. The bar-anvil cartridge proved unsatisfactory since the anvil was sometimes thrown into the barrel, and also the crimps in the case so close to the head resulted in occasional bursting of the copper case. In view of this, Martin patented in 1869 his folded-head construction, known as Martin-primed, and a little later in 1870 he made a slight improvement to his basic design. The manufacture of these Martin cartridges was abandoned in December 1871.

Several other types of inside-primed cartridges were experimented with during this period, such as the disc anvil, and others. However, the only type to be produced for general use was the Benet type. Colonel S. V. Benet, Comdg. Frankford Arsenal, introduced in 1868 the cup-anvil type, inside-primed, center-fire cartridge with solid head. At first the cup was constructed of tin, but this proved unsatisfactory since damp weather destroyed the fulminate priming. To remedy this situation, the cup was constructed of copper in 1870. The Benet-primed was the most successful of all inside-primed cartridges, and remained in use until it was replaced by the brass-cased, center-fire cartridge with external primer.

All cartridges shown have copper cases.

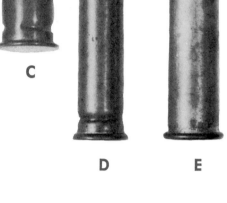

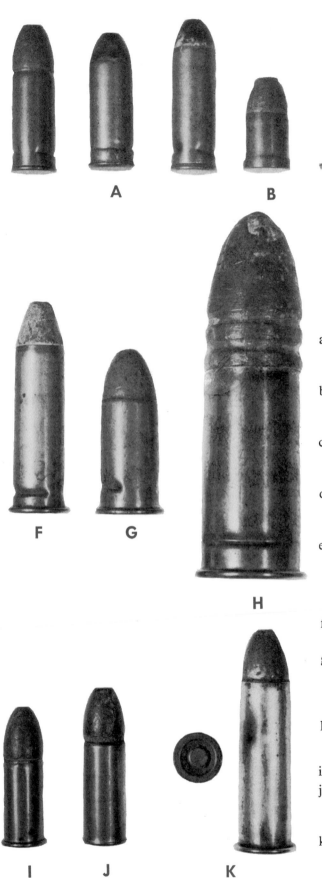

a. *one .44 and two .45 caliber Benet-primed cartridges* used in the first Colt cartridge revolvers.

b. *12mm cartridge* used in the French Perrin revolver which saw service in the American Civil War.

c. *.50 caliber Benet-primed cartridge* brought out in 1865 for use in the Remington rolling-block pistol.

d. *45-70-405 Benet-primed, government-rifle cartridge* made at the Frankford Arsenal in 1882.

e. *50-70-450 bar-anvil type cartridge* used in the altered Springfield muskets. These were made at the Frankford Arsenal between 1866 and 1868.

f. *50-70 Benet-primed cartridge* made at the Frankford Arsenal for Springfield rifles.

g. *.58 caliber Benet-primed cartridge* used in the early breech-loading muskets which were altered from the muzzle-loaders after the Civil War.

h. *One inch inside-primed Gatling gun cartridge* with 8 ounce bullet.

i. *.44 caliber S & W Martin-primed cartridge.*

j. *.44 caliber Colt-Remington Martin-primed cartridge.* Alongside is shown a base view of this cartridge.

k. *50-70-450 Martin-primed government cartridge* made only from May to December, 1871.

CENTER-FIRE · Modern

Colonel Hiram Berdan of the United States Army is credited with the invention of the drawn brass cartridge case. The case was made by forcing a disc of annealed brass through a series of dies to form the head of heavier brass than the walls. The brass case was much stronger than the earlier copper cases, and with the heavy head a pocket could be formed to hold an outside primer.

Two types of primers were used in conjunction with the brass cartridge cases with outside primers. The Berdan primer did not contain its own anvil, but instead was crushed against an anvil which was an integral part of the primer pocket. The base of this pocket was pierced with several holes to allow the fire to reach the propellant powder charge. The other type of outside primer contained its own anvil, and this complete unit was inserted in the primer pocket located in the head of the case. In this instance, there was only one hole in the bottom of the pocket to admit the flash. Today, the Berdan-type primer is most popular in Europe, while the primer containing its own anvil is most popular in the United States, since it is much easier to remove and reload.

The metal-jacketed bullet with a lead core was invented in Switzerland about 1880, either by a Major Bode or a Major Rubin. In 1832, a French chemist named Braconnet found that nitrocellulose, or guncotton, could be made by washing starch or cotton in nitric acid. This substance was extremely explosive and unstable, and it was not until 1885 that another French chemist, Vieille, discovered that by reducing nitrocellulose with solvents it could be made to burn in a controlled fashion. This led to the development of the first smokeless powder. In 1888, Alfred Nobel of Sweden added nitroglycerin to the guncotton, resulting in a different smokeless powder known as ballistite.

By the late 1880's, with the brass cartridge case, metal-jacketed bullet, and smokeless powder, the modern center-fire cartridge was a reality, and it has remained basically unchanged to the present time.

A significant improvement in 1927 was made by the introduction of a non-corrosive primer, which left no harmful deposit in the barrel after firing.

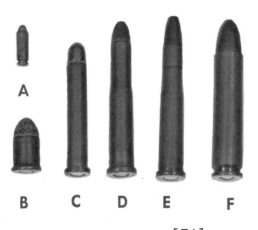

A

B   C   D   E   F   G

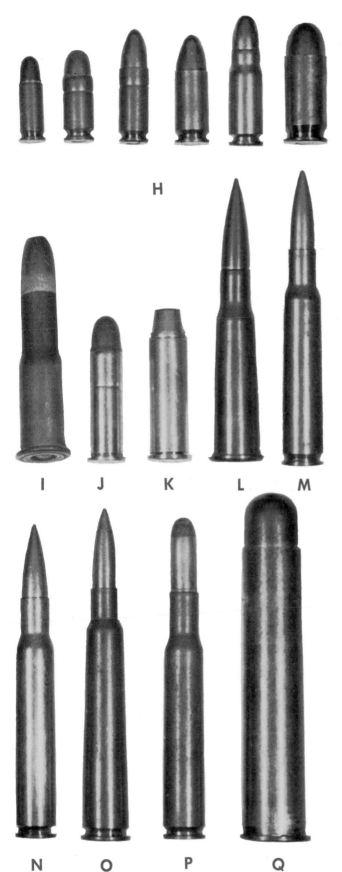

a. *The smallest center-fire cartridge* is the 2.7mm Kolibri, used in the German Kolibri automatic.

b. *.32 caliber cartridge* used in the Protector Palm pistol which was popular in the "gay nineties" era.

c. *5.5mm cartridge* used in the small European Velo Dog revolver.

d. *.22 caliber* used in the Winchester single-shot rifle in the early 1900's.

e. *.22 caliber Hornet cartridge* with metal-jacketed bullet.

f. *.30 caliber cartridge* used in the M1 carbine in World War II.

g. *.351 and .401 caliber self-loading cartridges* used in hunting rifles. These cartridges are metal-jacketed with soft point.

h. A grouping of *automatic-pistol cartridges.* From left to right are: .25 caliber, .35 caliber S & W, .30 caliber Pederson, 9mm Luger, 7.63 Mauser, and the .45 automatic Colt.

i. *40-50 paper-patched cartridge* used in the Sharps sporting rifle.

j. *.38 special,* the most popular revolver cartridge today in this country.

k. *.44 Magnum,* the most powerful revolver cartridge in the world, with a muzzle energy of 1150 foot-pounds.

l. *8mm cartridge* used in the French Lebel military rifle. The Lebel was one of the first to use smokeless powder, and was the official service cartridge of France in World Wars I and II.

m. *7 x 57 cartridge* used in the German Mauser rifle.

n. *30-03 American government cartridge* used in the Model 1903 Springfield rifle.

o. *30-06,* used in the Springfield rifle since 1906, and in World Wars I and II.

p. *.280 caliber high velocity cartridge* used in the Canadian Ross sporting rifle.

q. *English Kynoch .600 Nitro cartridge.* The bullet weighs 900 grains, and it is used in double-barrel rifles for hunting big game.

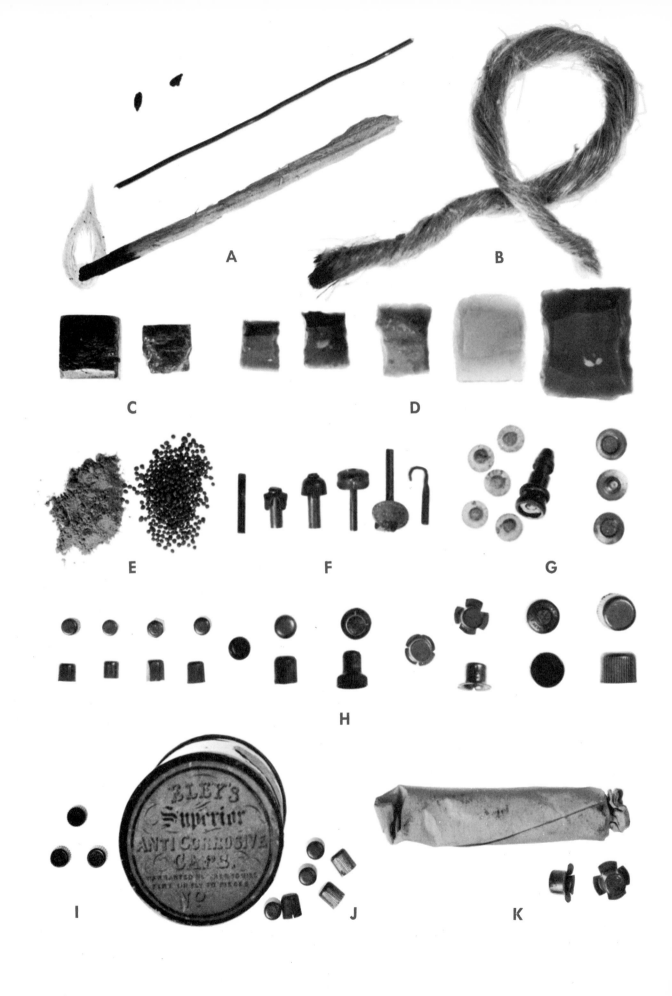

A

B

C

D

E

F

G

H

I

ELEY'S
Superior
ANTI CORROSIVE
CAPS.
WARRANTED NOT USED TO MISS
FIRE OR FLY IN PIECES
NO

J

K

PRIMERS

Pictured in this section are the primers, or primings, which were used to supply the flame or spark necessary to ignite gunpowder.

a. The first form of hand firearm, the hand cannon, was fired by inserting a match, live coal, or a heated wire, in the touch hole.

b. With the invention of the matchlock, a 3 or 4 foot length of matchcord, made from twisted strands of hemp, flax, or similar material, was placed in the serpentine. The matchcord was soaked in a solution of saltpeter for slow, steady burning, and both ends were lighted to increase the chances of a light always being available. The specimen of matchcord shown is made from flax.

c. A piece of iron pyrite, commonly called fool's gold, was used in wheellock weapons to provide the spark needed for ignition. Pyrite was usually used in preference to flint, since the former was softer, and consequently did not score the wheel as it rubbed against it.

d. Various types and sizes of flint, ranging from small pistol to musket sizes.

e. Fulminate of mercury in powder and pill, or pellet, form. Fulminating compounds are salts, which are produced by the dissolution of metals, such as mercury, silver, etc., in acids. When struck a blow, fulminates will explode, producing the necessary ignition for gunpowder. Fulminate was first used as loose powder. Later, a binding agent was added so that it could be shaped into pills or pellets. These pills were then given a protective coating of varnish or wax.

f. Tube primers were made in a number of different shapes to fit into the vents of tube lock guns made by various makers. The six types of tube primers illustrated, from left to right, are as follows: Manton primer. Joseph Manton was the inventor of the tube lock system. One drawback to his primers was the fact that when the tube was struck in the middle, flame spurted out both ends of the tube. To remedy this, most primers were pinched at the end protruding from the barrel. Westley Richards primer, commonly known as the mushroom primer. This was inserted in the nipple and held in place by pinching the petal-shaped flanges around the outside of the nipple. The primer is detonated when struck on its end by the hammer. This type of primer was very efficient and seldom misfired. Another form of the mushroom primer. Charles Lancaster primer, also commonly referred to as a hooded, or umbrella, primer. Primer with a clip to secure it to the gun. The brass plate is stamped "Alfred Clayton Patent." Primer equipped with a hook which fastened to the anvil.

g. Paper patch primings with a small quantity of fulminate sandwiched between thin pieces of paper. Paper patches were pressed into the end of a detachable striker, as shown alongside the patches, and the striker was then snapped into the hammer of the firearm. Next to the paper patches are several primers resembling them, except that the fulminate is located in the center of a copper disc, with the fulminate exposed on one side. The gun which used this primer is not known.

h. An assortment of metal percussion caps, showing pistol, military musket, and large game or punt gun sizes.

i. A different type of percussion cap, in which the fulminate is placed in a depression on the outside of the cap, rather than inside. In this instance, the cap was fitted onto the hammer, rather than onto the nipple, as was the case with all of the caps shown above.

j. A tin of Eley's percussion caps for revolvers.

k. A paper-wrapped packet containing 12 percussion caps. These caps were packed in a box along with 12 percussion cartridges for the Gallager breech loading carbine. This cap was commonly used on military arms and was known as the "top-hat" type.

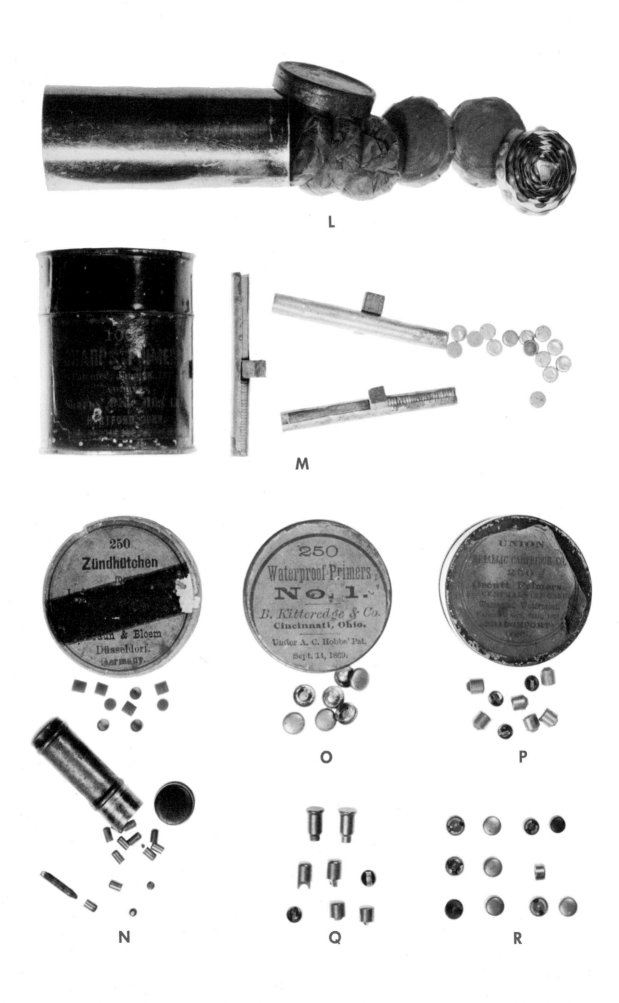

L

M

250
Zündhütchen

aun & Bloem
Düsseldorf.
Germany.

250
Waterproof Primers
No. 1.
B. Kitteredge & Co.
Cincinnati, Ohio.
Under A. C. Hobbs' Pat.
Sept. 14, 1869.

UNION
METALLIC CARTRIDGE CO.

O

P

N

Q

R

l. A waterproof can containing 10 rolls of Maynard tape primers. One roll has been unwrapped to show how the mounds of fulminate are placed between two narrow strips of paper, cemented together. The similarity of a roll of tape primers to a roll of caps for a toy pistol can easily be seen. The tape primer was patented by a dentist, Dr. Edward Maynard, on September 22, 1845.

m. A can for Sharps disc primers containing 40 tubes. Twenty-five of these disc primers were placed in the brass tube. The wooden block is used to strip the discs from the tube into the primer compartment of the gun. This primer consists of two circular halves of thin copper foil, pressed together, with fulminate in the middle.

PRIMERS, OR CAPS, FOR CARTRIDGES

n. A box of caps used to prime pin-fire cartridges. The cap is placed inside the cartridge case, and a pin, shown with the caps, has one end inserted in the open end of the cap, with the other end protruding from the rear of the case. Pin-fire cartridges are easily reloadable with the proper tool. The tubular brass container also holds another variety of caps used in pin-fire cartridges.

o. A box of Berdan brass primers. Berdan primers do not have built-in anvils. Instead, they are crushed against an anvil that is an integral part of the cartridge head. Most of the primers today have built-in anvils; however, a good many cartridges are currently being manufactured which use Berdan type caps.

p. A box of primers with built-in anvils. These copper primers were made by the Union Metallic Cartridge Company, and the box is marked "Orcutt Primers, central fire cases, patented Oct. 24, 1871."

q. A grouping of some early primers containing built-in anvils.

r. Some examples of late and modern type cartridge primers with built-in anvils.

PART IV

Revolvers

A BRIEF HISTORY OF REVOLVING FIREARMS

. . . . beginning with revolving matchlock weapons and progressing to the first Colt revolvers produced in 1836.

THE SMITH AND WESSON STORY

. . . . an historical digest of the Smith and Wesson association, starting a few years prior to the formation of their partnership and continuing to the present day firm.

"LEGAL EVASION" AND "INFRINGEMENT" REVOLVERS

. . . . the legal evasion and patent infringement revolvers, other than Smith & Wesson, that were spawned by the Rollin White patent.

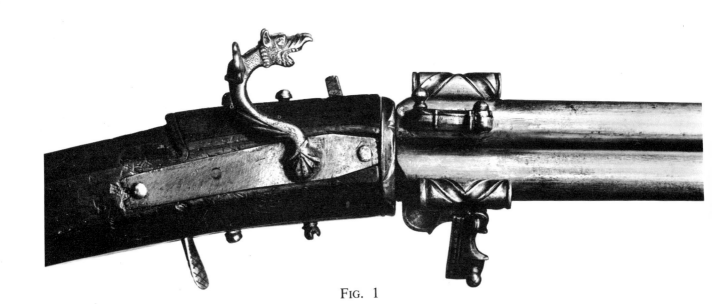

FIG. 1

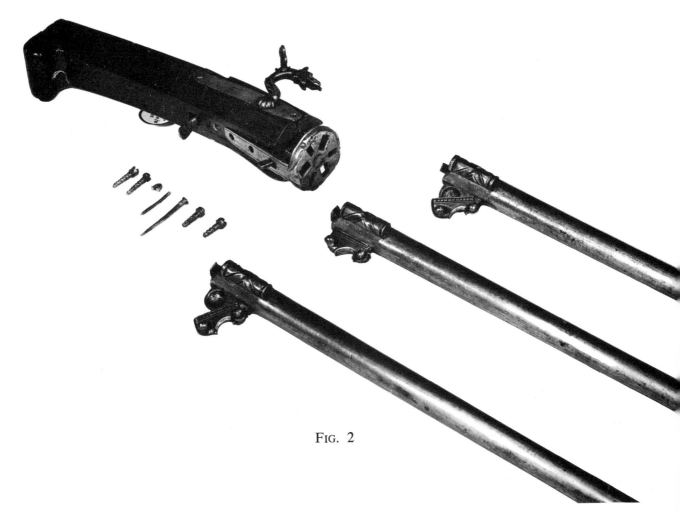

FIG. 2

A BRIEF HISTORY OF REVOLVING FIREARMS

For the purpose of this section concerning revolver history, the term "revolvers" will refer to handguns with a number of cylinders which can be revolved to shoot through a common fixed barrel and fire with a single striker or hammer. Pepperbox firearms, which can be defined as hand firearms with three or more full-length barrels encircling a central axis, firing shots successively with only one striker, are not included in this discussion, even though the majority of them had revolving barrels. A detailed account of pepperboxes can be found in the book entitled "Pepperbox Firearms" by Lewis Winant.

The first revolving weapons were crudely made matchlock muskets. The nature of the matchlock ignition system was not conducive to a revolving mechanism, however, and consequently very few were made. In the Palazzo Ducale in Venice, there is a specimen of a rare matchlock revolving pistol, as shown in figures one and two. The first weapons of fine workmanship to employ the revolving principle were snaphaunce petronels. In the Royal Museum of Arms in Copenhagen, there is a six-chambered revolving petronel dated 1597 and made in Nuremberg, indicating that this type weapon was in use before the close of the sixteenth century. See figure three.

Although the petronel cylinder had to be rotated by hand, there is a specimen in the Royal United Services Museum in London in which the cylinder is mechanically rotated 1/6 of a revolution whenever the action is cocked. In design, as well as mechanical operation, this snaphaunce revolver is very similar to Colt's first single-action percussion revolver patented almost 200 years later in 1836. This revolver measures 21½" overall, and the cylinder and barrel are both made of brass. Although there is no maker's name or marking on it, it can be dated around 1650 because of its similarity to single-shot pistols of this period.

No mechanically revolving handguns were made from the time of the snaphaunce revolver pictured in figure four to Colt's first percussion revolver. However, a "machine gun" was patented in 1718 in England by James Puckle. As can be seen in figure five, it bears a striking resemblance to the Gatling gun. In this gun, a turn of the handle revolved the cylinder, and at the same time a cam action automatically tripped and cocked the flintlock mechanism as each chamber lined up with the barrel.

Just before the close of the flintlock era, Elisha Haydon Collier introduced a flintlock revolver, as shown in figure six, which was greatly superior to any revolving-type firearm produced previously. Had it not been invented at a time when the flintlock was being made obsolete by the percussion detonating system, it would no doubt have brought about earlier development of the revolving principle in firearms. Collier, an

[83]

FIG. 3

FIG. 4

FIG. 5

American, patented his revolving firearms in London in 1818. Although the cylinders for the Collier pistols were hand-rotated, the outstanding feature of his invention which made it far superior to any previous development was his method of insuring cylinder and barrel alignment with a minimum escape of gas at the junction of the cylinder and the barrel. The cylinder of the pistol contained five chambers. The pan cover was equipped with an unique self-priming device consisting of a small box that contained enough fine powder to prime about a dozen shots.

two- or four-barreled "turnover" type pistols which were used just prior to the percussion cap. The heavy weight and the relatively short barrels of the pepperboxes prevented accurate shooting, and, as could be expected, gunmakers sought to remedy this situation. The man responsible for the first revolving pistol which was to become the prototype of all modern revolvers was Samuel Colt. His revolving pistol was patented in February, 1836 (incidentally, only one month before an application for a similar patent was received from a pepperbox manufacturer) and was produced at the

FIG. 6

With the advent of the percussion cap at about the same time that Collier produced his revolvers, it is strange that he did not utilize this ignition system, which was later to make the revolving principle a practical success. Only about 200 revolving weapons of all types were made by Collier between 1818 and 1821, and, evidently discouraged by the meager success of his flintlock weapons, he closed his gun shop in 1821 and devoted his efforts to engineering.

With the first patent of the percussion cap in 1818, the way was paved at last for a truly practical revolving pistol. The first revolvers that were made utilizing the percussion system were the pepperboxes, and they were probably an outgrowth of the

Colt factory in Paterson, New Jersey during the years 1836-1842. Shown in figure seven is a cased set of Paterson Colt pistols, complete with all accessories. These pistols were known as the Texas Models, and were the first to be manufactured at the Paterson plant primarily for use by the Texas Rangers.

The main features of the Colt patent called for a mechanically rotated cylinder fitted with horizontal nipples that were separated from each other by partitions. When the gun is cocked, a pawl connected to the hammer acts against a toothed ratchet wheel cut on the base of the cylinder, causing the cylinder to revolve. Another feature of the Colt design was the manner in which the cylinder was locked in position for firing. This was accomplished by means of a spring-loaded cylinder catch that engaged slots at the end of the cylinder adjoining the rifled barrel.

Critics of Colt made personal attacks upon him, claiming that he purported to be the first inventor of revolving arms. The fact is that Colt himself never made any such claim, either in his original patent of 1836 or for that matter at any time thereafter. The Colt factory in Paterson failed in 1842 due to insufficient orders, and was relocated in Whitneyville, Connecticut in 1847, and moved to Hartford, Connecticut in 1848 where it is still doing business today. Colt enjoyed a virtual monopoly for the manufacture of revolvers in this country until the expiration of his patent in 1856. His English patents, however, expired in 1851.

It was during this period, in 1855, that an obscure inventor named Rollin White obtained a patent for a revolver having the chambers of the cylinder bored through from front to rear. Combustible paper cartridges were to be used, with ignition provided by the use of a Maynard tape primer firing through a pierced cardboard wad. This wad was ostensibly meant to be used as a breechblock. White took his patent to Samuel Colt, who told him that it was worthless, as there was only a wad of cardboard between the shooter and the powder, and the charge most assuredly would have exploded out the rear of the gun. Had Colt seen the possibilities of the bored-through cylinder feature to be used in conjunction with a metallic self-contained cartridge, he would have enjoyed the exclusive manufacture of weapons firing this new type of ammunition. He died in 1862, and thus did not live to see the consequences of his rejection of White's patent, which was to play such a vital part in the Smith and Wesson story which follows.

FIG. 7

THE SMITH & WESSON STORY

On August 21, 1849, the United States Patent Office issued a patent to a New Yorker named Walter Hunt, for a repeating gun that was designed to fire what he referred to as a "rocket ball." This gun was the granddaddy of the famed Winchester tubular magazine repeating mechanism. Ammunition similar to Hunt's had been patented in England earlier. In 1841, two Englishmen named Hanson and Golden obtained a British patent on a hollow-base bullet which was to use fulminate of mercury for both detonator and propellant. They never designed a gun to shoot this bullet. In 1847, another Englishman named Stephen Taylor also obtained a patent for a hollow-base bullet containing black gunpowder. This bullet was covered with a cap containing a touchhole, and detonation was to be accomplished through the use of a percussion cap or other explosive material. At the same time, Taylor described a gun with a reservoir tube located below the barrel, from which a bullet was pulled up into the breech.

Several months after Hunt's patent was granted, another American named Lewis Jennings received a patent for a repeating rifle embodying an improvement on Hunt's weapon. His rifle had a tubular magazine containing the projectiles located underneath the barrel Bullets were fed to the barrel from below through the operation of a ringed trigger, with detonation from a Maynard tape primer. The Jennings arms were produced by the gunsmith firm of Robbins and Lawrence of Windsor, Vermont. Because of the ammunition used, these guns lacked the necessary wallop, and, as a result, were a complete failure.

A gunsmith named B. Tyler Henry, who worked at the Robbins and Lawrence plant, foresaw the potentialities inherent in the repeating mechanism, and had further improved the effectiveness of the weapon by substituting a lever at the front of the trigger guard in lieu of the ringed trigger. Evidently Henry did not have the money necessary to secure a patent, for he went to Worcester, Massachusetts, where he had formerly worked, and contacted Horace Smith, who was one of the best gunsmiths in the trade. Henry informed Smith that the Jennings rifle was a failure and was soon to be discontinued, and also told him of his improvement on it. Some time after this conference, Smith received a patent dated August 26, 1851, for a repeating gun with still further refinements to the Jennings weapon. No doubt Henry was partly responsible for these new ideas, but his name was not associated with the patent papers. Nothing was done in regard to producing this new invention until 1854, when Smith formed a partnership with Daniel B. Wesson.

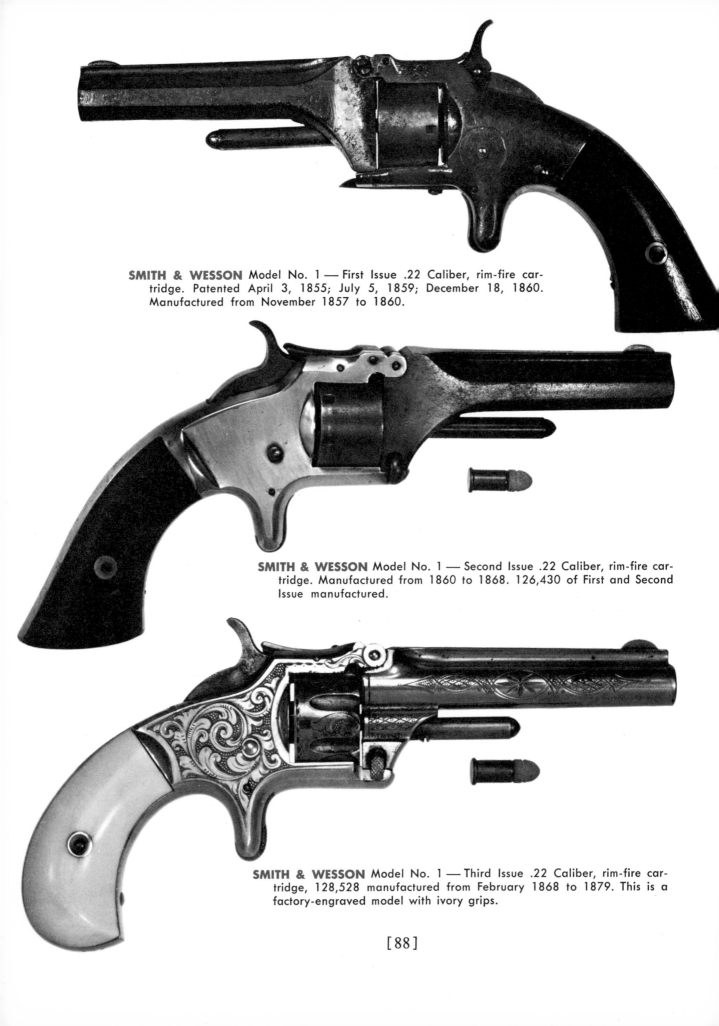

SMITH & WESSON Model No. 1 — First Issue .22 Caliber, rim-fire cartridge. Patented April 3, 1855; July 5, 1859; December 18, 1860. Manufactured from November 1857 to 1860.

SMITH & WESSON Model No. 1 — Second Issue .22 Caliber, rim-fire cartridge. Manufactured from 1860 to 1868. 126,430 of First and Second Issue manufactured.

SMITH & WESSON Model No. 1 — Third Issue .22 Caliber, rim-fire cartridge, 128,528 manufactured from February 1868 to 1879. This is a factory-engraved model with ivory grips.

Wesson was the brother of Edwin Wesson, the inventor of the Wesson-Leavitt revolver with hand-turned cylinder. Edwin Wesson died about 1850, and left to Daniel and his other heirs a patent application for an improved revolver with a mechanically operated cylinder. This legacy later resulted in one of the most famous lawsuits in the history of firearms. The heirs formed the Massachusetts Arms Company, and began production of this revolver, which in some respects was superior to Colt's revolver. Colt brought a successful suit for infringement of his basic patent. Although he made no demands for damages from the Massachusetts Arms Company, they nevertheless were deterred from making revolvers with mechanically turned cylinders.

In 1853, both Smith and Wesson were working for Allen, Brown and Luther, a firm specializing in gun barrels, in Worcester, Massachusetts. In that year, they formed a partnership, and manufactured cartridges and guns until 1855, when they sold out to the Volcanic Arms Company, headed by Oliver Winchester, a shirt manufacturer and former governor of Connecticut. The Volcanic Arms Company failed, and in 1857 Winchester formed the New Haven Arms Company, with Tyler Henry as plant superintendent. Henry, by the end of 1858, had developed a .44 caliber rim-fire cartridge. The Volcanic repeating mechanism was altered to fire this new ammunition, and the modified weapon was patented in Henry's name in 1860. About 1866, the New Haven Arms Company was reorganized, and renamed the Winchester Repeating Arms Company, and produced its first metallic cartridge weapon, known as the Model 1866.

When Smith & Wesson sold out to Oliver Winchester, there was a gentleman's agreement to the effect that Winchester would never compete in the revolver business, and Smith and Wesson would never compete in the rifle business. To this day, this agreement has never been broken.

Smith & Wesson had fared very well in the business of manufacturing lever action repeating arms, and left Norwich, after selling out to Winchester. They moved to Spring-field, Massachusetts, and continued experimenting with metallic cartridge revolvers while waiting for the Colt revolver patent to expire in the fall of 1857. Wesson continued his work on cartridge development.

In 1854, Smith & Wesson had been awarded a patent for a center-fire cartridge which contained tallow sandwiched in between the lead ball and powder charge. At the same time, Wesson developed a model revolver to accommodate these cartridges. He knew of the bulleted breech caps which were being produced in France by a man named Flobert. These Flobert caps were loaded with only fulminate of mercury, and when Wesson experimented with these cartridges in his revolver, they bulged and jammed between the cylinder and frame. The center-fire cartridge that Wesson had developed was impractical because of the expense involved in their manufacture. In attempting to solve this dilemma, Wesson came up with a rimmed cartridge in which a small space remained where the rim joined the cartridge case. Fulminate was inserted into this space, to be exploded when the hammer struck the rim of the cartridge. After perfecting a rim-fire cartridge which could be produced economically, Smith & Wesson prepared a patent application for a revolver to shoot these cartridges. This revolver was to be breech-loaded, and had its cylinders bored through from front to rear.

Shortly afterwards, they received a letter from the patent office in Washington informing them that the bored-through cylinder feature had already been patented by Rollin A. White of Hartford, Connecticut, on April 3, 1855. Smith & Wesson realized the importance of White's patent, and purchased the patent rights from him in 1856. After being turned down by Samuel Colt, White must have been pleasantly surprised to learn that Smith & Wesson considered the patent to be of value.

The exact details of the contract between Smith & Wesson and White are not known; however, we do know that White reserved the right to manufacture these revolvers under his own name, since he did produce a limited number of them. He also was to receive a royalty on each revolver manufactured, with the stipulation that he would bear all legal cost involved in any future patent infringements. More will be said concerning both legal evasions and patent infringements later in this section. Rollin White's future inventions in connection with firearms were inconsequential, but he had much greater success with his other inventions. Among them are the White Sewing Machine, and an early automobile, the White Steamer, which later grew into the White Bus and Truck Company.

Being in possession of the White patent, Smith & Wesson busied themselves by setting up a plant, hiring skilled workers, and preparing to go into production when Colt's patent would expire in the fall of 1857. In November, 1857, Smith & Wesson's first revolvers were ready for the market. These were the first cartridge revolvers produced in the United States. The .22 caliber seven-shot revolver was very popular, although it had little stopping power. By 1860, the firm was so successful that they moved to larger quarters, also in Springfield.

No doubt it must have bothered Smith & Wesson to have perfected such a revolutionary design embodying waterproof and easy-to-load metallic cartridges, and an efficient revolving mechanism, only to have the end product regarded as practically a toy. Although Smith & Wesson's competitors were manufacturing large caliber percussion revolvers which did not fire the efficient metallic cartridge, they nevertheless packed a wallop, which was a vital necessity during this period.

The chief obstacle to producing a revolver of larger caliber was the fact that the copper cartridge case had to be thin enough to be dented by a blow from the hammer, and yet thick enough to withstand the powder explosion. When the first Smith & Wesson cartridges were made, the methods of handling copper were such that the largest caliber which could be produced in a cartridge was the .22. A few years later, an unknown coppersmith perfected a method of annealing copper, which toughens the metal without making it brittle.

This development made it possible to produce copper cartridges of a larger caliber.

To meet the demand for larger caliber arms during the Civil War, Smith & Wesson brought out the Model 1½, a .32 caliber six-shot revolver. While still not as deadly as the .44 caliber cap and ball revolvers, they could be loaded much more quickly, with waterproof ammunition, and Smith & Wesson had to work their plant on night shifts to meet the demand for these revolvers by officers in the Civil War.

Smith & Wesson's 14-year patent rights for the bored-through cylinder feature were due to expire on April 3, 1869, and many manufacturers were waiting to start production on a revolver of this pattern. The following year, 1870, Smith & Wesson came out with their first large caliber revolver which was the .44 caliber Model 3 American. In addition to selling a number of these guns to the public and the United States Army, Smith & Wesson sent a model of this revolver to the Russian Military Attache in the United States. At the request of the Russian government, they made slight modifications, resulting in what has come to be known as the Model 3 Russian. During a seven-year period, 150,000 large caliber revolvers of various types were sent to Russia.

Another modification to the Model 3 American was made by Colonel George Schofield. These changes amounted to a barrel catch improvement, and an increase in caliber from .44 to .45. Figuring that they would secure a government contract, Smith & Wesson permitted Schofield to patent these changes in his own name in a patent dated April, 1873, and the new revolver was known as the Schofield.

About 1873, Horace Smith retired, and sold his interest in the business to Wesson. It was agreed that the firm would continue under the name of Smith and Wesson. Smith died on January 15, 1893, and Wesson on August 4, 1906. Wesson's three sons took over management of the business, and its affairs are directed today by the present generation of Wessons.

The three .22 caliber Smith & Wesson revolvers shown are the First Model, 1st, 2nd, and 3rd Issues.

LEGAL EVASION AND INFRINGEMENT REVOLVERS OF THE SMITH & WESSON PATENT

This portion dealing with evasions and infringements of the Smith & Wesson patent was written by LEWIS WINANT.

THE FIRST of the famous .22 rim-fire Smith & Wesson First Model revolvers was hardly out of the shop before flagrant infringements were being produced in quantity, and advertised for sale, by such manufacturers as Allen, Bacon Arms Co.; F. D. Bliss, Lowell Arms Co.; J. P. Lower, Moore's Patent Firearms Co.; L. W. Pond; E. A. Prescott; and James Warner. Two rarities, the Albert Christ two-barreled 18-shot revolver, and the Edward Sneider two-cylinder revolver, were infringements produced in small numbers.

There would have been no immediate and widespread infringing of the patent if there had not been great doubt by most manufacturers — a doubt shared even by Smith & Wesson — as to the validity of Smith & Wesson's patent.

There were other manufacturers (American Standard Tool Co., Deringer, J. M. Marlin — to name three) that brought out close copies of early Smith & Wesson revolvers, but they were not guilty of infringement, because their imitations were not marketed until the Smith & Wesson patent expired.

The Smith & Wesson revolver fired metallic self-contained cartridges that were loaded from the rear into a cylinder *with its chambers bored completely through.* Chambers in cylinders of percussion-cap revolvers had not been bored through. Messrs. Smith and Wesson were all ready to manufacture their invention when it came to their notice that a Rollin White had, shortly before, been granted a U. S. patent for a percussion-cap revolver having chambers "extending through the rear of the cylinder for the purpose of loading them at the breech from behind." Smith and Wesson knew that the fantastic revolver devised by Rollin White was of no value. They also knew that a pepperbox-revolver, with the cylinder bored through and loaded from the rear, was being manufactured in France, and that George Leonard had received a U. S. patent, five years before, covering firearms' barrels "drilled and bored entirely through." It was reasonable to believe the claim of novelty in the Rollin White patent would not stand up in court.

But Smith & Wesson further knew that their position would be stronger if they controlled the Rollin White patent. Accordingly, they made an agreement with White to let them manufacture their revolvers under his patent, paying him a royalty, with the understanding that White would defend his patent claims against infringement.

In some cases no more than a letter from Smith & Wesson to an offending manufacturer was needed to get his production of imitations stopped. In other cases, resort to court action was necessary, and large production of illegal copies did not cease until the Federal Circuit Court in the District of Massachusetts, in November, 1863, gave a verdict in favor of Smith & Wesson.

No other firearms manufacturer ever came so close to having a patent thrown out by the U. S. Supreme Court as did Smith & Wesson. The 1863 Circuit Court's decision was appealed by a defendant, Allen, and it was not until February 8, 1869, less than two months before the Smith & Wesson patent expired, that the Supreme Court upheld the lower court, by a vote of four to four. (A tie vote always upholds the lower court's decision.)

The Civil War Smith & Wesson revolvers were made only in .22 and .32 calibers, and most of the infringers were of similarly small caliber with little stopping power. Notable exceptions were the .38's made by Prescott, and the .44's made by Allen & Wheelock, and by Pond.

James Reid went further than others who violated the Smith & Wesson patent. He provided revolvers with chambers bored through for .32 rim-fire cartridges, then he threaded those chambers and supplied nippled inserts which were screwed in from the rear and permitted the revolvers to be used with cap and ball.

We now go from the illegal copies to the lawful, ingenious, and interesting evasions — those revolvers with chambers that were not bored through and those that were not loaded from the rear.

Of the successful evasions that were marketed — more than a score did not get beyond the experimental stage and will get no mention here — the first and perhaps the best type was the front-loading cup-primer revolver, made by Plant's Manufacturing Co., New Haven; by Eagle Arms Co., New York; and by Connecticut Arms Co., Norfolk, Conn. The first patent granted for a revolver cylinder using a cup-primer, or "hollow-base" cartridge was U. S. 24,726 of July 12, 1859. A further patent that "simplified the construction of the cylinder" was 30,318 of July 21, 1863. Although both of these patents were taken out by Wilbur Ellis and John White (apparently not related to Rollin White) they were assigned to other men, especially Ebenezer and Amzi Plant, partners in Plant's Manufacturing Co., which was located first in Southington, Connecticut, and later in New Haven.

The "cup-primer," or "hollow-base" cartridges were different from rim-fires in that "They are made without the laterally projecting flanges . . . but have flanges projecting in a rearward direction or parallel with the bores of the chambers to contain the fulminate priming." The cylinders were not bored entirely through, but were constructed with a small round opening at the rear to allow the nose of the hammer to strike the interior of the hollowed base of the cartridge which had been pressed in from the front of the chamber. This construction left at the rear of the chamber an annular shoulder which was an adequate recoil shield.

The earliest Plant revolvers were of hinged-frame construction; the later Plants, and all the Eagle and the Connecticut Arms revolvers, were solid-frame.

The Plant revolvers of .42 caliber were intended for Army use, but as they were not purchased by the U. S. Government they are not classed as martial revolvers; the Eagle and the Connecticut Arms revolvers of small caliber were designed as pocket arms.

It should not be thought that the early Smith & Wesson revolvers were inevitably superior to the Plant front-loaders and the other evasions. Smith & Wessons could be loaded more quickly, but men who bought revolvers for self-defense did not expect to be given time for reloading.

The cartridges of the front-loading evasions were perhaps less safe when being loaded, but they had no rims to be deformed by blows of the hammer, with the possible result of jamming a cylinder.

Unfair arguments that sold many front-loaders were that inasmuch as the explosive force of all gunpowder acted backward as well as forward the open rear of a Smith & Wesson cylinder caused energy to be wasted and bullet velocity reduced, and that Smith & Wessons had only frail recoil shields to back the cartridges and protect shooters.

Probably the most widely sold of the evasions were the teat-fire front-loaders made under Daniel Moore's U. S. patent 38,321 of April 28, 1863. That patent covered the formation of the cylinder so as to prevent the use of a rear-loading cartridge, but leaving an opening barely a sixteenth of an inch across through which a teat of a front-loading cartridge would protrude. This fulminate-filled protuberance — sometimes flat, sometimes round — at the center of the cartridge base received the hammer blow. Some of these revolvers bear the name Moore; others, National. Nearly all are of .32 caliber, but a few exist in .45 caliber.

The first successful evasion revolver to use a conventional rim-fire cartridge was the Slocum Patent Side-Loading Revolver. It was easily loaded and unloaded without being taken apart. The Slocum's cylinder was closed at its rear except for slots for the hammer nose. It had rounded troughs, open only at the front, fitted with sliding tubes which functioned as chambers. Loading required that the hammer be brought to half cock and a tube pushed forward until a cartridge could be dropped sideways into a trough. After a little practice, the operation was quickly completed. The illustration shows a Slocum just after a cartridge has been placed in a trough. By turning the revolver on its side the cartridge will fall out, as will an empty shell in the same circumstances when unloading. The Slocum probably was made in .32 caliber only.

Another evasion using regular rim-fire cartridges was the Pond Separate-Chambers Revolver, made in seven-shot .22 caliber and in six-shot .32. The Ponds had chambers which enclosed "lining-thimbles" which themselves held the rim-fire cartridges. One

of these open-end thimbles with a cartridge pressed in up to its rim easily fitted into a chamber. The cylinder is, of course, not bored through, but its rear edge is pierced with notches through which the hammer nose gets through to the cartridge rim. The removable thimbles were loaded and unloaded from the rear, but the cartridge-filled thimbles themselves were front loaded into the chambers, thereby circumventing Smith & Wesson's patent.

A revolver that fired 12 millimeter pinfire cartridges and was still able to avoid patent infringement was the scarce Polain. Prosper Polain, of Belgium, patented this in the United States, March 27, 1866, patent 53,548. The Polain revolver had the side-loading feature of the Slocum and the thimbles feature of the Pond.

The scarcest of the evasions, not counting some that never got past the patent model stage, are the Crispins, patented by Silas Crispin, October 3, 1865, U. S. patent 50,224. When the hinged-frame Crispin is opened for loading, the barrel tips down and the cylinder comes apart into two right circular divisions, the forward part being connected to the barrel and the rear to the frame. To load, the bases of the peculiar cartridges are pushed back into the not-bored-through rear of the cylinder. Then, upon closing the gun, each cartridge is half in the front and half in the rear of the cylinder and functions as does a dowel pin so that the front of the cylinder necessarily rotates in unison with the rear as the rear is revolved by the usual ratchet with the cocking of the hammer.

Cartridges for the Crispin revolvers are sought by collectors as eagerly as are the revolvers themselves. The Crispin cartridge was patented by Silas Crispin two months before he patented his revolver, and could be used only in a gun with a divided chamber. Crispin's cartridge patent, 49,237, specified "fulminate placed within a projecting annular recess or rim, which is formed at a point between the ends of the cartridge case." The construction provided an efficient gas check and easy removal of a fired case with the fingers, but that fulminate-filled belt around its mid-section (where the long-nosed hammer struck) invited premature explosion.

If we assume all of the guns considered to be in the same condition, good to fine, a Thuer Colt, the last of the Smith & Wesson evasions, not only may well be the most desired of the Colt cartridge revolvers, but also of all Colt revolvers it is outranked in value only by the Walker and the Paterson models.

This elaborate late-comer was brought out when the Smith & Wesson patent had less than a year to run. It was not manufactured in great numbers, and as its manufacture was discontinued when the Smith & Wesson patent ran out, a good example is hard to find.

Thuer Colts were revolvers converted by Colt from Colt percussion-cap revolvers of .31, .36, or .44 caliber. A Thuer Colt is not only the last of the Smith & Wesson evasions, but it also is the first Colt to use metallic cartridges, and the first American revolver produced for all-metal, self-primed, reloadable cartridges.

A complete Thuer Colt outfit included two cylinders — one of which could be used with cap and ball, the other with Thuer cartridges — with a five-piece tool for reloading those special cartridges.

The Thuer conversion was a special cylinder invented and patented by F. Alexander Thuer, September 15, 1868, United States patent 82,258. The Thuer cylinder was produced by turning down the rear of a percussion cylinder far enough to expose the ends of the chambers, but not deep enough to interfere with operation of the cylinder-turning ratchet, and fitting an intricate ring equipped both with a firing pin and an ejecting lever in place of the turned-off portion. That annular ring was capable of sideways movement, independent of the cylinder. With the ring turned fully clockwise by a thumbpiece, the firing pin was driven by the hammer against the head of the cartridge in line with the barrel. When the ring was turned fully back, snapping the hammer caused the ejecting lever to throw out a fired case from the chamber second to the right from the hammer.

The Thuer Colt employed a metallic tapered-to-the-rear, center-fire, reloadable cartridge which was front-loaded by the conventional rammer used to load Colt percussion-cap revolvers.

All of the front-loading evasions used peculiar metallic cartridges, but not all of the unorthodox metallic cartridges of the time were front-loaded. Some writers have classed revolvers that fired lip-fire cartridges as evasions. Actually, the lip-fire revolvers produced before the Smith & Wesson patent expired were clearly infringements. They all had chambers bored completely through, and their cartridges were loaded from the rear.

Pictured on the following pages are twelve revolvers which successfully evaded the Smith & Wesson patent, followed by examples of two revolvers that were infringements of this patent.

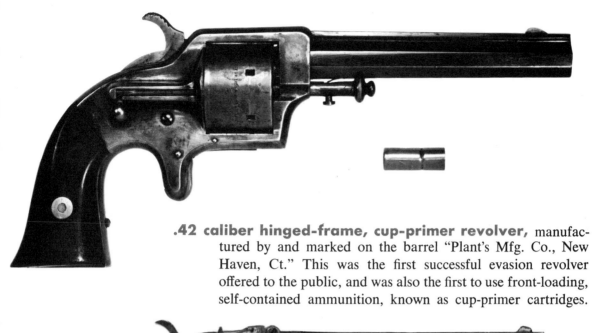

.42 caliber hinged-frame, cup-primer revolver, manufactured by and marked on the barrel "Plant's Mfg. Co., New Haven, Ct." This was the first successful evasion revolver offered to the public, and was also the first to use front-loading, self-contained ammunition, known as cup-primer cartridges.

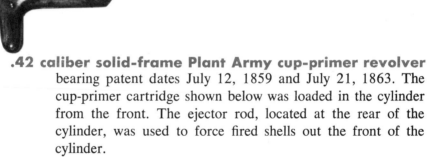

.42 caliber solid-frame Plant Army cup-primer revolver bearing patent dates July 12, 1859 and July 21, 1863. The cup-primer cartridge shown below was loaded in the cylinder from the front. The ejector rod, located at the rear of the cylinder, was used to force fired shells out the front of the cylinder.

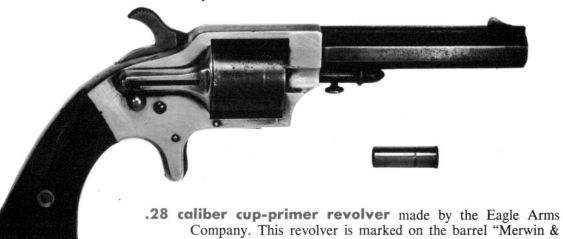

.28 caliber cup-primer revolver made by the Eagle Arms Company. This revolver is marked on the barrel "Merwin & Bray Firearms Co., N. Y." Merwin & Bray were sales agents for these weapons.

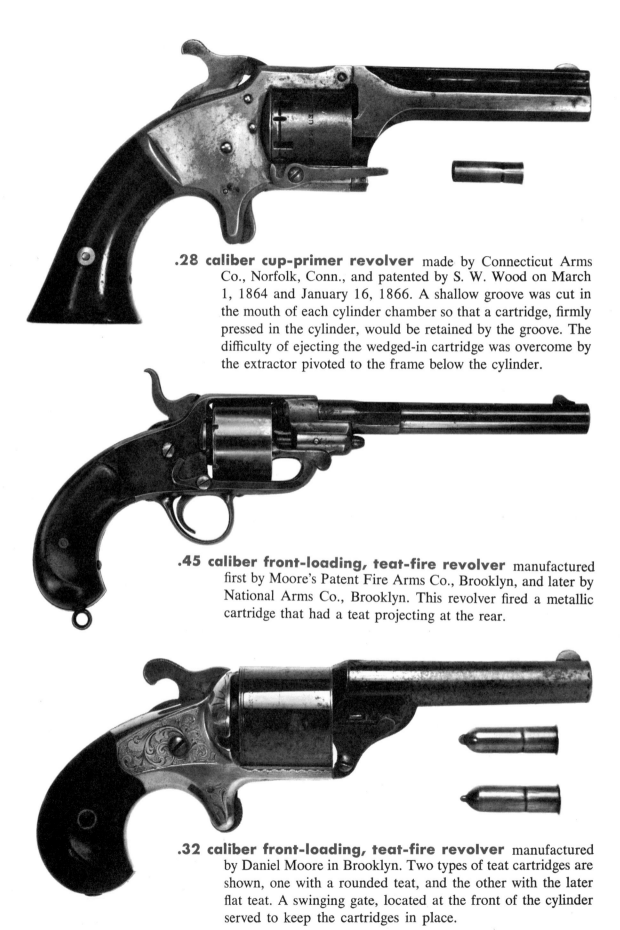

.28 caliber cup-primer revolver made by Connecticut Arms Co., Norfolk, Conn., and patented by S. W. Wood on March 1, 1864 and January 16, 1866. A shallow groove was cut in the mouth of each cylinder chamber so that a cartridge, firmly pressed in the cylinder, would be retained by the groove. The difficulty of ejecting the wedged-in cartridge was overcome by the extractor pivoted to the frame below the cylinder.

.45 caliber front-loading, teat-fire revolver manufactured first by Moore's Patent Fire Arms Co., Brooklyn, and later by National Arms Co., Brooklyn. This revolver fired a metallic cartridge that had a teat projecting at the rear.

.32 caliber front-loading, teat-fire revolver manufactured by Daniel Moore in Brooklyn. Two types of teat cartridges are shown, one with a rounded teat, and the other with the later flat teat. A swinging gate, located at the front of the cylinder served to keep the cartridges in place.

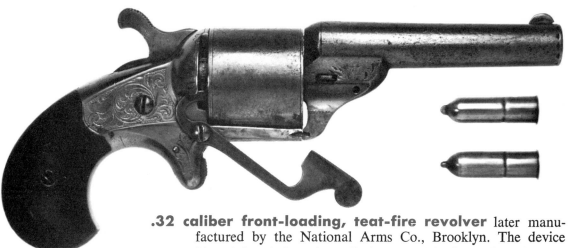

.32 caliber front-loading, teat-fire revolver later manufactured by the National Arms Co., Brooklyn. The device hinged just below the cylinder served both to eject the cartridges, and to keep them in place in the cylinder. The teat revolvers enjoyed the largest sales of all the front-loading revolvers.

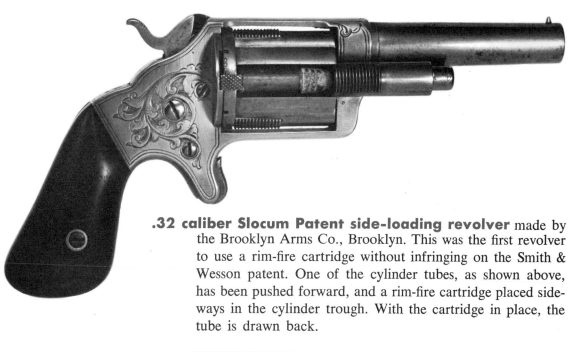

.32 caliber Slocum Patent side-loading revolver made by the Brooklyn Arms Co., Brooklyn. This was the first revolver to use a rim-fire cartridge without infringing on the Smith & Wesson patent. One of the cylinder tubes, as shown above, has been pushed forward, and a rim-fire cartridge placed sideways in the cylinder trough. With the cartridge in place, the tube is drawn back.

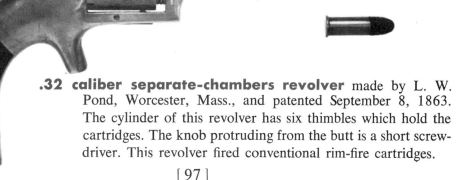

.32 caliber separate-chambers revolver made by L. W. Pond, Worcester, Mass., and patented September 8, 1863. The cylinder of this revolver has six thimbles which hold the cartridges. The knob protruding from the butt is a short screwdriver. This revolver fired conventional rim-fire cartridges.

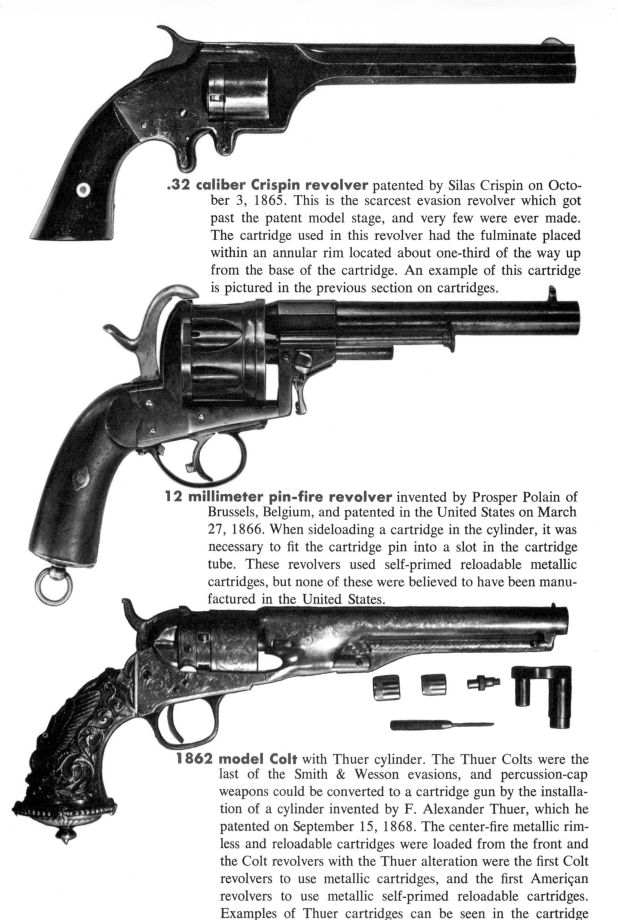

.32 caliber Crispin revolver patented by Silas Crispin on October 3, 1865. This is the scarcest evasion revolver which got past the patent model stage, and very few were ever made. The cartridge used in this revolver had the fulminate placed within an annular rim located about one-third of the way up from the base of the cartridge. An example of this cartridge is pictured in the previous section on cartridges.

12 millimeter pin-fire revolver invented by Prosper Polain of Brussels, Belgium, and patented in the United States on March 27, 1866. When sideloading a cartridge in the cylinder, it was necessary to fit the cartridge pin into a slot in the cartridge tube. These revolvers used self-primed reloadable metallic cartridges, but none of these were believed to have been manufactured in the United States.

1862 model Colt with Thuer cylinder. The Thuer Colts were the last of the Smith & Wesson evasions, and percussion-cap weapons could be converted to a cartridge gun by the installation of a cylinder invented by F. Alexander Thuer, which he patented on September 15, 1868. The center-fire metallic rimless and reloadable cartridges were loaded from the front and the Colt revolvers with the Thuer alteration were the first Colt revolvers to use metallic cartridges, and the first American revolvers to use metallic self-primed reloadable cartridges. Examples of Thuer cartridges can be seen in the cartridge section.

.32 caliber seven-shot revolver made by Daniel Moore in Brooklyn, and patented by him on September 18, 1860. As can be seen, the cylinder swings out to the right for loading by pressing the catch alongside the hammer. This revolver is one of 18,057 unsold revolvers turned over to Smith & Wesson by four companies in settlement of damage claims for infringement of the Smith & Wesson patent. This revolver is stamped on the barrel "Manfd. for Smith & Wesson by Moore's Pat. Fire Arms Co."

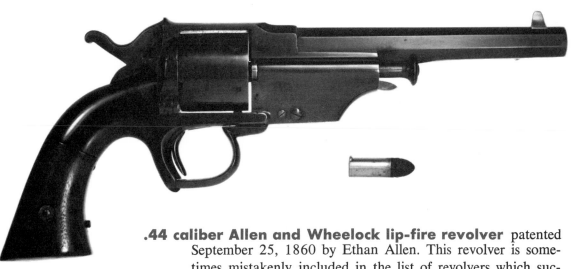

.44 caliber Allen and Wheelock lip-fire revolver patented September 25, 1860 by Ethan Allen. This revolver is sometimes mistakenly included in the list of revolvers which successfully evaded the Smith & Wesson patent. The cartridge fired in this gun is shown below, and fulminate was placed in the protruding lip at the base of the cartridge. The cylinder chambers were completely bored through, and the lip-fire cartridges were breechloaded; therefore, this revolver was an infringement rather than an evasion. A slot was cut in the rear of the cylinder, and it was necessary to place the cartridges in such a way that the lip lined up with the slot.

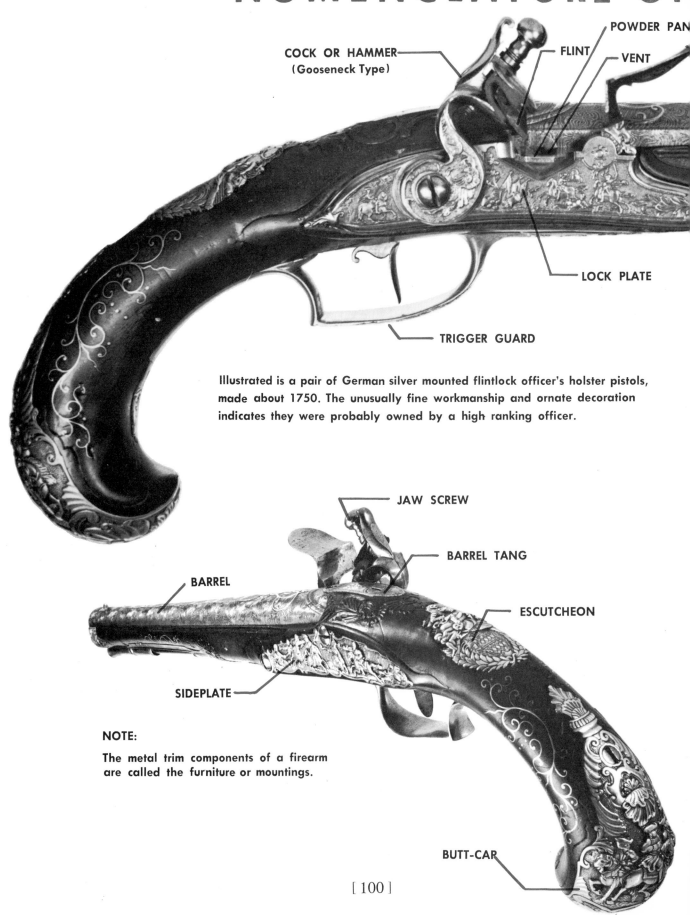

COCK OR HAMMER
(Gooseneck Type)

FLINT

POWDER PAN

VENT

LOCK PLATE

TRIGGER GUARD

Illustrated is a pair of German silver mounted flintlock officer's holster pistols, made about 1750. The unusually fine workmanship and ornate decoration indicates they were probably owned by a high ranking officer.

JAW SCREW

BARREL TANG

BARREL

ESCUTCHEON

SIDEPLATE

NOTE:

The metal trim components of a firearm are called the furniture or mountings.

BUTT-CAP

A FLINTLOCK PISTOL

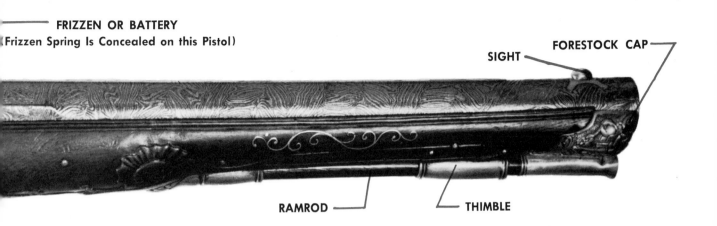

FRIZZEN OR BATTERY
(Frizzen Spring Is Concealed on this Pistol)

SIGHT

FORESTOCK CAP

RAMROD

THIMBLE

INTERIOR OF LOCK MECHANISM

(This lock is from a Kentucky rifle, made around 1790.)

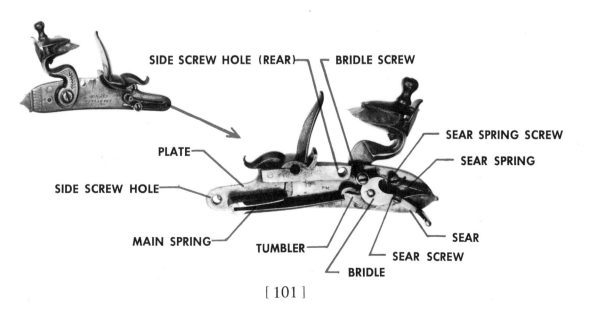

SIDE SCREW HOLE (REAR)

BRIDLE SCREW

PLATE

SEAR SPRING SCREW

SEAR SPRING

SIDE SCREW HOLE

MAIN SPRING

TUMBLER

SEAR SCREW

SEAR

BRIDLE

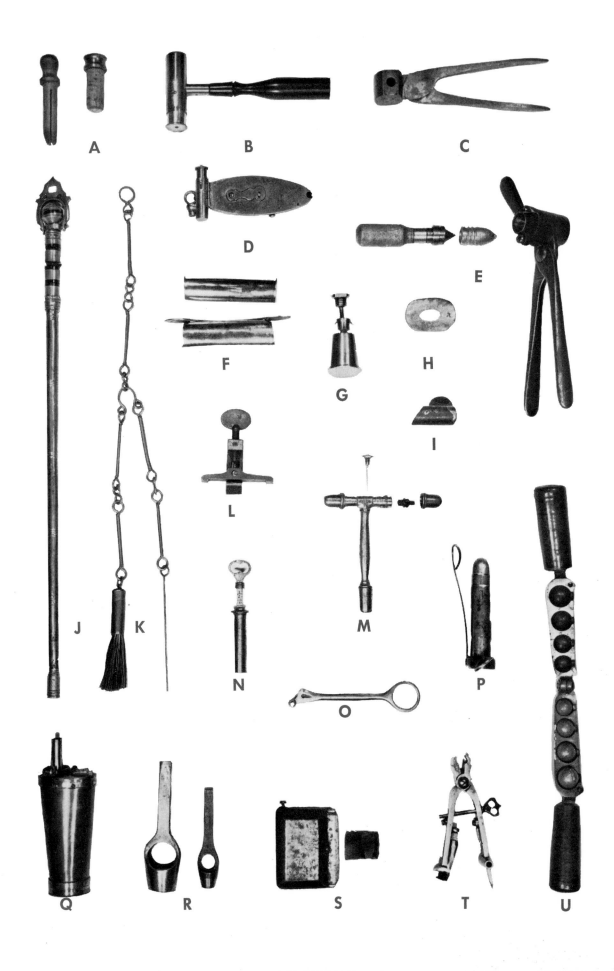

A   B   C

D

E

F

G   H

I

J   K   L   M   P

N   O   U

Q   R   S   T

MISCELLANEOUS TOOLS AND ACCESSORIES FOR FIREARMS

All items are pictured approximately ⅓ of their actual dimensional size.

a. Wooden tompion (left) and cork tompion with brass cap. These were inserted in gun barrels to keep out moisture.

b. Graduated shot and powder measure for shotguns, made by Parker Brothers.

c. Bullet mold from a cased set of duelling pistols.

d. Brass percussion cap dispenser equipped with device for priming nipple opening with fine powder.

e. Two-piece .58 caliber mold set for casting Minie balls. A Minie ball is shown with the mold.

f. Shot and powder chargers for flintlock shotguns. A partition is located midway in each charger. The bottom charger is pictured with both end caps opened.

g. English oiler with threaded top.

h. A thin piece of lead which is wrapped around a flint to secure it in the jaws of a cock, or hammer.

i. Tin scoop for measuring powder and shot.

j. Middle Eastern sneath, which is a combination knife sharpener and pistol ramrod. This tool was usually carried by horsemen. The top is attached to a pair of long tweezers, concealed inside the long rod. These tweezers were used to pick up a live coal for lighting tobacco.

k. Military picker and brush set for flintlock musket.

l. Spring vise for removing lock spring, circa 1850.

m. Nipple wrench, with pick shown unscrewed from the top. One of the knobs has also been removed to show how a replacement nipple can be carried in the wrench.

n. Graduated powder measure, or charger, from a cased set of muzzle-loading percussion duelling pistols.

o. Tool for extracting headless type shells from a shotgun.

p. Brass tool for reloading pin-fire cartridges.

q. Flask from a cased set of flintlock duelling pistols. This flask has three compartments: for powder, lead balls, and spare flints.

r. Two sizes of steel cutters used to make wads for cartridges. Large size wad cutters were also used to make patches which were wrapped around balls fired in rifled firearms.

s. Eighteenth century steel tinderbox used to make a flame. A piece of flint, carried inside the compartment, is struck against one side of the tinderbox to generate a spark. These sparks, falling onto a bed of finely shredded flax, or tow, produce a flame.

t. Combination tool for percussion firearms.

u. Gang mold from the Revolutionary War period, for making four round musket balls of different sizes.

BIBLIOGRAPHY

Early Percussion Firearms by LEWIS WINANT

English Pistols and Revolvers by J. N. GEORGE

English Guns and Rifles by J. N. GEORGE

Cartridges by HERSCHEL C. LOGAN

The American Cartridge by CHARLES R. SUYDAM

Small Arms and Ammunition in the United States Service
   by BERKELEY R. LEWIS

The Age of Firearms by ROBERT HELD

Gas, Air and Spring Guns of the World by W. H. B. SMITH

Air Guns by ELDON G. WOLFF

Air-Guns and Air-Pistols by L. WESLEY

Smith and Wesson Hand Guns by ROY G. MCHENRY and WALTER F. ROPER

Series entitled "The Cartridge . . . Its History and Evolution," published in
   The American Rifleman, by CHARLES T. HAVEN